MW00627604

MODEL CURRICULUM FOR TRAINING BUILDING INSPECTOR REFRESHER COURSE FOR ACCREDITATION UNDER TSCA SECTION 206

Revised by:
Safety, Health, and Ergonomics Branch
Electro-Optics, Environment, and Materials Laboratory
Georgia Tech Research Institute
Atlanta, Georgia 30332

U.S. Environmental Protection Agency
Cooperative Agreement
No. CX 820760-01-0

EPA Project Officer: Karen Hoffman
Office of Pollution Prevention and Toxics
U.S. Environmental Protection Agency
401 M Street, SW
Washington, D.C. 20460

Published by
ehsMaterials.com

ISBN # 13:978-0-9789435-8-5
2015

MODEL CURRICULUM FOR TRAINING BUILDING INSPECTORS

PREFACE

This manual was developed to provide guidance and assistance for those individuals who will conduct a building inspection for the presence of asbestos-containing materials. The procedures and practices detailed in these pages incorporated recent technology at the time of publishing. The reader is reminded that as technology evolves, so do the methods for conducting building inspections. Therefore, we emphasize the need for the reader to obtain the most up-to-date information available.

Originally developed in response to the U.S. Environmental Protection Agency's Asbestos Hazard Emergency Response Act (AHERA), the procedures and practices presented in this manual provide detailed information on how to conduct comprehensive building inspections in compliance with AHERA, yet also go beyond the basic regulatory framework to include inspection practices which can be adopted and adapted for many situations. Hence provisions of the U.S. Occupational Safety and Health Administration's worker protection regulations as well as EPA'S Asbestos School Hazard Abatement Reauthorization Act (ASHARA) and the National Emission Standards for Hazardous Air Pollutants) (NESHAP) are included.

Professionals in the field of asbestos detection and control developed this manual. Throughout its preparation, the manuscript was subjected to external review in government, academic, and industry circles.

The technical expertise and common sense brought to an inspection by the Building Inspector are major components of a successful asbestos management or abatement program. The reader is encouraged to improve further upon the techniques provided in this manual as he or she gains additional knowledge through field practice.

ACKNOWLEDGEMENTS

This model curriculum was originally prepared under sponsorship of the U.S. Environmental Protection Agency. Environmental Sciences, Inc., of Tucson, Arizona was responsible for managing the original development effort, with the Environmental Science and Technology Laboratory of the Georgia Tech Research Institute providing technical input and other general support in all areas of curriculum development.

Individually, the Georgia Tech Research Institute would like to express its gratitude to Karen Hoffman and Robert Jordan, PH.D., of the U.S. EPA's Office of Pollution Prevention and Toxics, Chemical Management Division, Field Programs Branch. Mrs. Hoffman served as Project Officer for this revision, and her comments and direction were helpful in keeping the project moving to completion, and in producting a quality product. Dr. Jordan provided technical comment and review, as well as regulatory update. Mr. Jack Primack of the Field Programs Branch provided helpful technical editing of this material as well.

This update represents the dedication and hard work of the original developers of this manual, plus the efforts of many individuals who contributed their time and expertise to these revisions. Those individuals within the Georgia Tech Research Insitute who assisted in the reviisions to this document include Robert Schmitter, who served as Project Manager, Vicki Ainslie, Myrtle Turner-Sippio, David Jacobi, C.I.H., and Gayle Goeway. Acknowledgement also goes to the many support personnel for their help.

Georgia Tech wishes to acknowledge the contributions of those individuals who assisted in revising this manual by providing helpful comments and advice:

Tom Broido, ATC-Dennison Environmental Services, Richmond, VT, Mark Demyanek, C.I.H., C.S.P., Board of Regents, U of Georgia, Atlanta, GA, John Dietrichs, Environmental Aspecs, Inc. of Georgia, Roswell, GA, Mike Durbin, C.I.H., Durbin Environmental Consultants, Inc., Duluth, GA, Bill Echoes, A.I.A., Gobble Hays Partners, Inc., Nashville, TN, Toni Hurley, C.I.H., Robins Air Force Base, Warner Robins, GA, Neal Smith, M.S.P.H., J.D., RERC Environmental, Atlanta, GA

MODEL CURRICULUM FOR TRAINING
ASBESTOS BUILDING INSPECTOR REFRESHER

TABLE OF CONTENTS

KEY TO ABBREVIATIONS

ACM	Asbestos Containing Material
ACBM	Asbestos-Containing Building Material
AHERA	Asbestos Hazard Emergency Response Act
ASHARA	Asbestos School Hazard Abatement Reauthorization Act
CFR	Code of Federal Regulations
CPSC	Consumer Product Safety Commission
DOT	Department of Transportation
EL	Excursion Limit
EPA	Environmental Protection Agency
FR	Federal Register
f/cc	Fibers per cubic centimeter
FWPCA	Federal Water Pollution Control Act
HEPA	High Efficiency Particulate Air
LEA	Local Education Agency
MAP	Model Accreditation Plan
MSHA	Mine Safety and Health Administration
NESHAP	National Emission Standards for Hazardous Air Pollutants
NIOSH	National Institute of Occupational Safety and Health
NIST	National Institute for Standards and Technology
NVLAP	National Voluntary Laboratory Accreditation Program
OPPT	Office of Pollution Prevention and Toxics (EPA)
OSHA	Occupational Safety and Health Administration
OTS	Office of Toxic Substances (Now Office of Pollution Prevention & Toxics)
PEL	Permissible Exposure Limit
RACM	Regulated Asbestos-Containing Material
TSCA	Toxic Substances Control Act
TWA	Time-weighted average

SECTION A: BACKGROUND INFORMATION ON ASBESTOS

HISTORICAL PERSPECTIVE

The word asbestos is derived from a Greek adjective meaning inextinguishable. The "miracle mineral" as it was referred to by the Greeks, was admired for its soft and pliant properties, as well as its ability to withstand heat. Asbestos was spun and woven into cloth in the same manner as cotton. It was also utilized for wicks in sacred lamps. Romans likewise recognized the properties of asbestos and it is thought that they cleaned asbestos tablecloths by throwing them into the flames of a fire.

From the time of the Greeks and Romans in the first century until its re-emergence in the 18th century, asbestos received little attention or use. It was not available in large amounts until extensive deposits were discovered in Canada in the late 1800s. Following this discovery, asbestos emerged as an insulating component in thermal system insulation for boilers, pipes, and other high temperature applications and as reinforcement material for a variety of products.

CHARACTERISTICS OF ASBESTOS

Asbestos is a naturally occurring mineral. It is distinguished form other minerals by the fact that its crystals form long, thin fibers. Deposits of asbestos are found throughout the world. The primary sites of commercial production are: the Commonwealth of Independent States, Canada, china, Brazil, Zimbabwe, and South Africa. Asbestos is also mined commercially in limited quantities in the United States, in California and Vermont.

Asbestos minerals are divided into two groups- serpentine and amphibole. The distinction between groups is based upon a minerals crystalline structure-serpentine minerals have a sheet or layered structure; amphiboles have a chain-like crystal structure.

Chrysotile, the only asbestos mineral in the serpentine group, is the most commonly used type of asbestos and accounts for approximately 95% of the asbestos found in buildings in the United States. Chrysotile is commonly known as "white asbestos," so named for its natural color.

Five types of asbestos are found in the amphibole group. Amosite, the second most likely type to be found in buildings, is often referred to as "brown asbestos." As you might assume, in its natural state it is brown in color.

Crocidolite, "blue asbestos," is also an amphibole. Crocidolite was used in high temperature insulation applications.

The remaining three types of asbestos in the amphibole group are: <u>anthophyllite,</u> <u>tremolite,</u> and <u>actinolite.</u> These varieties are of little commercial value. Occasionally they are found as contaminants in asbestos containing materials.

Once extracted from the earth, asbestos containing rock is crushed, milled (ground) and graded. This produces thread-like fibers of material. What actually appears as a fiber is an agglomeration of hundreds or thousands of fibers, each of which can be divided even further into microscopic fibrils.

USES OF ASBESTOS

Asbestos has been used in literally thousands of products. Collectively, these are frequently referred to as asbestos-containing material (ACM). Asbestos gained wide-spread use because it is plentiful, readily available, and low in cost. Because of its unique properties- fire resistance, high tensile strength, poor heat and electrical conductivity, and being generally impervious to chemical attacks, asbestos proved well-suited for many uses in the construction trades.

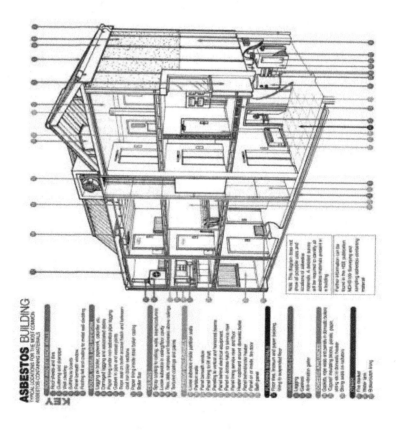

SECTION A: BACKGROUND INFORMATION ON ASBESTOS

One of the most common uses for asbestos is a fireproofing material. It was sprayed on steel beams, columns, and decking that were used in construction of multi-storied buildings. This application prevented these structural members from warping or collapsing in the event of fire. Chrysotile was the most commonly used asbestos constituent in sprayed-on fireproofing. Asbestos compromised 5 to 95 percent of the fireproofing mixture and was used in conjunction with materials such as vermiculite, sand, cellulose fibers, gypsum, and a binder such as calcium carbonate.

These materials are soft and may be fluffy in appearance and to the touch. They vary in color from white to dark gray and occasionally they have been pained or encapsulated with a clear or colored sealant. The material may be exposed or concealed behind a suspended ceiling. Application to structural members (beams ad columns) often resulted in some material being sprayed on walls and ceilings as well. This is referred to as overspray.

Asbestos is added to a variety of building materials to enhance strength. It is found in concrete and concrete-like products. Asbestos-containing cement products generally contain Portland cement, aggregate, and chrysotile fibers. The asbestos content may range up to 50 percent by weight depending on the use of the product. Asbestos cement products are used as siding and roofing shingles; as wallboard; as corrugated and flat sheets for roofing, cladding, and partitions; and as pipes. Asbestos has also been added to asphalt, vinyl and other materials to make products like roofing felts, exterior siding, floor tile, joint compounds, and adhesives.

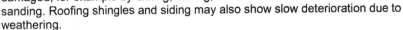

Fibers in asbestos cement, asphalt, and vinyl are usually firmly bound in the matrix and will be released only if the material is mechanically damaged, for example by drilling, cutting, or sanding. Roofing shingles and siding may also show slow deterioration due to weathering.

As an insulator, asbestos received widespread use for thermal insulation and condensation control. It was usually spray applied, trowel applied, or factory installed on or within equipment.

Asbestos proved valuable as a component of acoustical plaster. The material was applied by trowel or by spraying on ceilings and sometimes walls. It varies in color from white to gray-rarely was it painted as a noticeable loss of acoustical value occurs. Similarly, as a decorative product, asbestos was mixed with other materials and sprayed on ceilings and walls to produce a soft, textured appearance.

SECTION A: BACKGROUND INFORMATION ON ASBESTOS

FRIABLE VS. NONFRIABLE ACM

The U.S. Environment Protection Agency (EPA) distinguishes between friable and nonfriable forms of ACM. Friable ACM contains more than 1% asbestos and can be "crumbled, pulverized, or reduced to powder by hand pressure when dry." Other things being equal, friable ACM is thought to release fibers into the air more readily; however, many types of nonfriable ACM can also release fibers if disturbed.

CATEGORIES OF ASBESTOS-CONTAINING BUILDING MATERIALS

EPA identifies three categories of ACM used in buildings:
- **Surfacing Materials** – ACM sprayed or troweled on surfaces (walls, ceilings, structural members) for acoustical, decorative, or fireproofing purposes. This includes plaster and fireproofing insulation.

- **Thermal System Insulation** – Insulation used to inhibit heat transfer or prevent condensation on pipes, boilers, tanks, ducts, and various other components of hot and cold water systems and heating, ventilation, and air conditioning (HVAC) systems. This includes  pipe lagging, pipe wrap; block, batt, and blanket insulation; cement and "muds"; and a variety of other products such as gaskets and ropes.

- **Miscellaneous Materials** – Other, largely nonfriable products and materials such as floor tile, ceiling tile, roofing felt, concrete pipe, outdoor siding, and fabrics.

While it is often possible to "suspect" that a material or product is or contains asbestos by visual determination, actual determinations can only be made by instrumental analysis. The EPA requires that the asbestos content of suspect materials be determined by collecting bulk samples and analyzing them by polarized light microscopy (PLM). The PLM technique determines both the percent and type of asbestos in the bulk material. However, some of these materials do not have to be inspected and inventoried under the Asbestos Hazard Emergency Response Act (AHERA) Rule. Asbestos-containing building materials (ACBM) as defined by the Rule excludes materials installed outside a building (e.g., roofing felt and siding) and most fabric materials.

EVIDENCE OF HEALTH RISKS

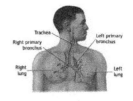

To understand the health risks associated with a substance such as asbestos, scientists evaluate date compiled from clinical, <u>epidemiological</u>, and laboratory studies. Clinical date ordinarily provide the first indication that a substance may have adverse effects on the body. Physicians observe a pattern of symptoms, or the presence of a disease which appears to be linked with a particular activity, or exposure to a particular substance. Such observations lead to a hypothesis that the activity or substance caused the symptoms or the observed disease. Epidemiologists will then undertake an investigation to attempt to confirm the hypothesis. If an association between the symptoms, or disease, and the activity or substance appears to be substantiated, laboratory studies are undertaken. Should animal response to the substance produce effects similar to that observed in humans, the case to an association is strengthened.

Most of the information on the health effects of exposure to asbestos has been derived from studies of workers exposed to asbestos in the course of their occupation. Asbestos fiber concentrations for such workers are many times higher than those encountered by the general public, or by most workers in buildings with asbestos-containing material (ACM). Because their exposure was much higher, asbestos workers will have a much higher incidence of asbestos-related diseases than people who live or work in buildings with ACM. This is known as the <u>dose-response</u> effect. However, people in buildings with ACM are still likely to experience higher risks than the public at large. Unfortunately, the available data does not allow us to reliably estimate the actual risk.

Because asbestos fibers appear to be ubiquitous, virtually everyone is exposed to some extent. During autopsy, asbestos fibers have been detected in the lungs of most urban residents. Exposure of the general public is troublesome because we are talking about a large population which includes unhealthy as well as healthy people. Moreover, exposure may begin during childhood, leaving a long period for the manifestation of asbestos-related disease. Furthermore, asbestos may enhance the carcinogenic effects of other materials. Any additional exposure to asbestos caused by living or working in buildings with ACM should thus be avoided.

Despite epidemiological studies of workers and laboratory studies of animals, questions remain about which properties of asbestos are responsible for the adverse health effects. It is not known whether the particular properties which produce on disease, for example, lung cancer, are the same as those which produce another disease, such as <u>asbestosis</u>. Which conditions of exposure are most likely to lead to adverse health effects have not been positively identified. Some characteristics that appear to be important are: the physical size of fibers (long, thin fibers seem to be the most toxic) and their durability. The variation in chemical composition among different types of asbestos does not appear to be as important as differences in physical properties. However, the Environmental

Protection Agency (EPA) believes that current evidence is not sufficient to say that one type is any more toxic than another.

Some natural substances other than asbestos seem to have health effects similar to those of asbestos. For example, erionite, a fibrous form of a mineral called zeolite, induces mesothelioma in test animals. Persons living in central Turkey, where this substance is found, are reported to have a higher than expected incidence of several disease associated with asbestos. These include mesothelioma, previously believed to be caused exclusively by asbestos.

Exposure to man-made mineral fibers, such as fibrous glass and ceramic materials is relatively recent. Occupational exposure levels have not been as high as asbestos exposure. Hover, some epidemiological data do suggest that diseases of the respiratory tract, such as pulmonary fibrosis and lung cancer, may results from long-term exposure to these fibers if the fibers are thing. It is generally accepted that many of these replacement insulation products have a thicker fiber diameter which makes them less respirable than the very thing fibers of the asbestos minerals. However, as manufacturing and extruding processes advance, some of these manufactured minerals are achieving thinner, more respirable diameters.

THE RESPIRATORY SYSTEM

To be a significant health concern, asbestos fibers must be inhaled. An understanding of the mechanics of the respiratory system will aid in appreciating the potential for exposure and the resulting health effects.

Every cell in the body needs a constant supply of oxygen. The respiratory system meets this need by bringing oxygen to the bloodstream, which delivers it to each ell and carries away carbon dioxide. The lungs are the focal point of the respiratory system, which also includes the respiratory tract, the channel by which air flows into and out of the lungs. Exhibit B-1 is an illustration of the respiratory system.

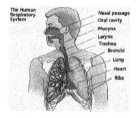

Inhaled air passes through the nose, where moisture and tiny hairs filter dust. It then passes down the throat where air is also humidified. Air continues into the trachea, a tube supported by rings of cartilage. Just above the heart, the trachea divides into two bronchi. Each bronchus leads into a lung where is subdivides into bronchioles and smaller air tubes, giving the appearance of an upside down tree. The tiniest tubes end in globular air sacs, or alveoli.

The actual exchange of gases-respiration- takes place in the alveoli. There, blood vessels only one cell thick allows oxygen and carbon dioxide to trade places. The carbon dioxide is exhaled back up the respiratory tract; the blood picks up fresh oxygen and transports it throughout the body.

The lungs, cone-shaped, balloon-like, elasticized tissue, are located on either side of the chest. Each lung is encased by a double layer of membrane, or pleura. One layer is attached to the lung, the other to the rib cage. Space and fluid between the two layers enable the lungs to expand and contract in the chest cavity without friction. To visualize this association, think of two panes of glass with a drop of water between them. The pieces of glass, like the linings, slide easily across each other, but are difficult to pull apart. When we breathe in, the diaphragm stretches out flat and muscles between the ribs contract with it, pulling the ribs up and out. This expands the chest cavity, creating a vacuum between the linings, that expands the lungs and sucks in air. When breathing out, the diaphragm and rib cage muscles relax, the ribs fall in and down, and the lungs contract and push out the carbon dioxide and unused oxygen.

The respiratory system is sensitive to bacteria, viruses, and many airborne particles than can be inhaled. Reactions to these irritants can disrupt the functioning of the system resulting in many ailments including the following: the common cold, hay fever, sinusitis, sore throat, acute or chronic bronchitis, emphysema, and lung cancer.

The body has several mechanisms by which it filters the air it breathes. The tiny hairs in the nose filter out dust and airborne particles. Like the nose, the trachea and the bronchi are lined with small fine "hairs "called cilia. Together with mucous secreted by cells lining the airways, cilia trap particles and help prevent respiratory infections. The cilia beat in an upward direction sweeping foreign particles up to the back of the mouth where they are expelled or swallowed. Viruses and bacteria are also attacked by enzymes called lysozymes in the mucous cells. Microbes that slip through are usually handled by white blood cells called macrophages that envelop and eat these invaders in the lung.

Cigarette smoking temporarily paralyzes the cilia. If smoking continues long enough, the cilia wither and die. They are never replaced. The efficiency of the cilia is replaced by the smoker's inefficient cough which attempts to ride the respiratory tract of foreign particles and excess mucous.

Dirty, contaminated air presents the greatest challenge to the respiratory system. Some of the particles entering the airways reach the alveoli. When this occurs, macrophages attempt to engulf and digest the particles. In the case of asbestos, we are dealing with a mineral fiber, a substance which macrophages can often not successfully attack. As a means of secondary defense, the macrophages deposit a coating of enzymes on the fibers which are then deposited in the smaller passages. Here they clog and actually scar the tissues. The walls of the alveoli lose

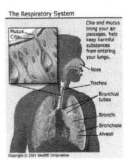

The Respiratory System

7

their elasticity and useful function in respiration. Coated asbestos fibers ("<u>asbestos bodies</u>") are often seen at autopsy.

DISEASES ASSOCIATED WITH ASBESTOS EXPOSURE

The adverse health effects of asbestos were observed in the first century by the Greeks and Romans. They noted a breathing problem in slaves weaving asbestos cloth. Modern knowledge linking asbestos and a lung disease called asbestosis dates to 1900. Autopsy reports from 1938-1949 indicated that a large number of persons who died with <u>asbestosis</u> also had lung cancer. IN the 1960s, the link between asbestos and a rare form of cancer called <u>mesothelioma</u> was established. These diseases are discussed below.

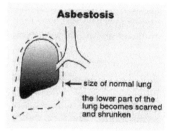

Asbestosis

<u>Asbestosis</u> is a scarring (fibrosis) of the lung. The scarring impairs the elasticity of the lung tissue and hampers its ability to exchange gases. This leads to inadequate oxygen intake to the blood. The disease restricts breathing leading to decreased lung volume and I increases resistance in the airways. These last two impairments make the actual act of breathing difficult. It is a slowly progressive disease with <u>latency period</u> of 10-20 years. Asbestosis is irreversible and may progress even after exposure to asbestos has ceased. The earliest symptom of asbestosis is often coughing. As the disease progresses, shortness of breath upon exertion is noted. Changes in pulmonary function (lung function), <u>rales</u> (crackling sounds in the lower half of the lung), and clubbed fingers are disease markers. As the disease advances, x-rays of the chest will help demonstrate the incidence of fibrosis, although a lung biopsy provides the only definitive diagnosis. Relatively high doses of exposure are needed before asbestosis is observed. While there is no cure for asbestosis, anyone suffering with the disease should be removed from further exposure as more disabling fibrosis can be prevented by eliminating further inhalation of asbestos fibers.

<u>Lung Cancer</u> is a malignant tumor of the bronchi covering. The tumor grows through surrounding tissue invading and often obstructing the air passages. The earliest symptom is often a persistent cough; a physical exam may attribute the symptoms to chronic bronchitis. Chest x-rays sometimes show shadows that indicate tumors and enlarged lymph nodes. However, the time between exposure to asbestos and the occurrence of lung cancer is typically 20 years. Although there are many causes of lung cancer, a clear increase in risk has been found among people who work with asbestos. Moreover, there is no threshold or limit of exposure below which the risk of lung cancer is not increased.

Mesothelioma is a cancer of the mesothelium, the lining of the chest or the lining of the abdominal wall. It is considered to be a marker disease for asbestos exposure. Early stages are associated with few symptoms. By the time it is diagnosed, it is almost always fatal. Effective therapy does not exist. There is no exposure threshold for

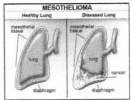

mesothelioma. This is suggested by the observation that family members of asbestos-exposed workers have developed mesothelioma. Presumably, cleaning the clothes of the exposed worker exposed these individuals to asbestos dust and led to the disease. Studies indicate that Crocidolite asbestos exposure is more closely linked to mesothelioma than other types of asbestos. However, it is very uncommon for an asbestos-exposed individual to be exposed to only one of the asbestos minerals. Similar to other asbestos-related diseases, mesothelioma has an extended latency period of 20-40 years.

Other diseases and adverse health effects have been noted among the population exposed to asbestos fibers. Increased incidence of non-respiratory cancers have been observed in some recent epidemiological studies. Cancers of the larynx, esophagus, stomach, colon-rectum, kidney, and pancreas are present at slightly higher than predicted levels. An abnormality found on x-rays of persons exposed to asbestos is <u>pleural plaque,</u> a fibrous thickening of the lining of the chest cavity. These are usually not symptomatic of asbestos diseases and require no treatment. However, they tend to increase the statistical likelihood of eventually developing lung cancer. Pleural plaques are found in exposed workers as well as in their family members. Plaques are also found in people living near mines,, shipyards, and manufacturing plants where asbestos is or was utilized.

SYNERGISTIC RELATIONSHIP BETWEEN ASBESTOS AND SMOKING

Cigarette smoking is the single most important known cause of lung cancer in humans. People who smoke 20 cigarettes per day increase their risk of developing lung cancer by ten-fold (10x) when compared to the non-smoker. Workers exposed to the same level of asbestos as insulation workers historically increase their risk of developing lung cancer by five-fold (5x). These two factors working together have a <u>synergistic</u> effect; the smoker exposed to asbestos fibers is at least fifty times (50x) more likely to develop lung cancer than the general public.

RISKS ASSOCIATED WITH LOW LEVEL EXPOSURE

Asbestos is known to be a carcinogen based on studies of asbestos workers and laboratory animals. However, the risks associated with low level, non-occupational exposure (for example, as an occupant of a building containing ACM) are not well established. Attempts have been made to estimate low level risks by extrapolation from occupational exposure data. This is not a straightforward process and its validity is questionable.

Based on a thorough review of the health effects literature, EPA concludes there is no level of exposure below which the risks of contracting an asbestos-related disease are zero. That is, there is no <u>threshold level</u> of exposure.

A 1984 survey sponsored by EPA[1] attempted to assess exposure to ACM in public and commercial buildings. According to the data, a lower percentage of public and commercial buildings contain friable ACM than do school buildings (20% vs. 35%). However, limitations in the data prevent firm conclusions regarding the number of persons exposed, exposure levels, or the exposure levels of service/maintenance workers in comparison with the public.

A mathematical model was developed by EPA in this 1984 study to assess risk. Risk calculations suggest that if asbestos exposure is eliminated in schools, we have the potential to significantly reduce the overall risk for this segment of our population which may later be exposed to asbestos in public and commercial buildings. It should be noted, however, that although the elimination of exposure in schools may reduce risk, there remains a risk as the result of exposure to asbestos elsewhere.

Asbestos fibers accumulate in the lungs. As exposure increases, the risk of disease likewise increases. Measures to minimize exposure and consequently minimize the accumulation of fibers reduce the risk of adverse health effects.

Despite the uncertainties associated with the risk of low level exposure, if we accept the fact that there is no safe level of exposure to asbestos, we have cause to institute measure to control or eliminate exposure; regulations such as AHERA move in this direction.

EXHIBIT B-1
ILLUSTRATION OF
RESPIRATORY TRACT

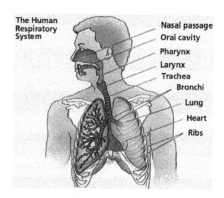

The Human Respiratory System

Nasal passage
Oral cavity
Pharynx
Larynx
Trachea
Bronchi
Lung
Heart
Ribs

SECTION C: FUNCTIONS, QUALIFICATIONS, AND THE ROLE OF BUILDING INSPECTORS

FUNCTIONS

Two U.S. Environmental Protection Agency regulations require the use of accredited Building Inspectors when conducting an inspection for the presence of asbestos. The Asbestos Hazard Emergency Response Act (AHERA), promulgated in 1986, requires that all schools, grades K-12, be inspected for the presence of asbestos-containing building material (ACBM).

This inspection must be conducted by an individual accredited as a Building Inspector whose work will provide the basic information upon which an AHERA-accredited Management Planner will estimate the degree of current or potential hazard posed by the ACBM, and develop a plan for managing the ACBM.

The Asbestos School Hazard Abatement Reauthorization Act (ASHARA), promulgated in 1990 and effective as of November 1992, requires that any asbestos inspection conducted in a public or commercial building be performed by an accredited Building Inspector. In both instances the Building Inspector will be responsible for (1) determining whether ACBM is present in a building and (2) assessing the physical characteristics of the ACBM within the building. (See Section L, "Regulatory Review" for more detail on these regulations).

QUALIFICATIONS

The Asbestos Emergency Response Act (AHERA) Model Accreditation Plan suggests minimum qualifications for Building Inspectors and Management Planners. In addition, some states have raised the suggested minimum requirements, adding qualifications and experience they deem appropriate.

EPA-Suggested Minimum Prerequisites

Inspectors	Management Planners
High School Diploma	Registered architect, engineer, CIH, or related scientific field.

To become an accredited Building Inspector, qualified persons are required to complete an EPA-or state-approved 3 day training course and obtain a minimum score of 70% on a written examination. To maintain their accreditation, Building Inspectors must attend an annual refresher course of one-half day in length. It is important to note that each state has the option of requiring persons to complete additional training and pass reaccreditation examinations at specific intervals.

OVERVIEW OF THE INSPECTION PROCESS

A building inspection involves (1) an investigation of records (including previous surveys, plans, specifications, and other documents) for the identification of ACBM, (2) a physical and visual inspection of the building for suspect materials, (3) sampling and analyzing suspect materials to test for asbestos, and (4) assessing the condition and location of the ACBM and other characteristics of the building. More specifically, the inspection process consists of the following steps:

- Review architectural and "as-built" (record) plans, work change orders, and other records for the specification of any materials which contain asbestos.
- Inspect the building for friable materials, and materials or products which are likely to contain asbestos.
- Delineate homogeneous sampling areas and develop sampling plan for bulk samples (or assume suspect material contains asbestos).
- Collect samples and have them analyzed for asbestos by an accredited laboratory.
- Collect information on the physical condition and location of all ACBM or other characteristics of the building which may affect the likelihood that ACBM may be disturbed and that fibers may be released and disturbed.

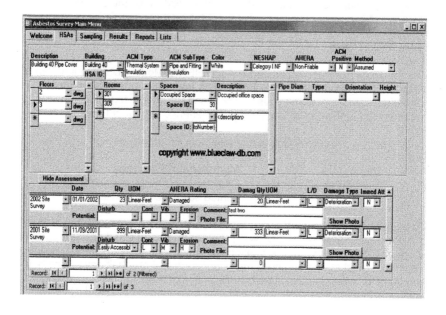

INTRODUCTION

Inspectors are exposed to liability due to the critical role they play in the asbestos management process. The inspection report will be the basis for all subsequent actions taken by the facility manager to control asbestos-containing materials. The assessment report provides guidance for the development of operations and maintenance strategies, the determination of response actions, and it is an integral part of any management plan.

If an asbestos Inspector fails to properly identify an area of asbestos-containing material in a facility, or improperly assess its condition, liability under several scenarios is possible. The facility owner may initiate a claim against the Inspector for breach of contract. Occupants of the facility who are exposed to asbestos as a direct result of a faulty assessment may claim personal injury. Contractors who proceed in reliance on a deficient assessment could sue the Inspector for injuries suffered as a result of exposures, delay or lost profits when they are surprised by the discovery of asbestos. If the facility owner is sued as a result of a deficient assessment, the Inspector would almost certainly become involved in the litigation as a third-party defendant.

LIABILITY OF INSPECTORS

The Inspector faces three areas of potential liability: regulatory, criminal, and civil.

REGULATORY LIABILITY

"..the first rule in addressing issues of environmental liability is not to assume that a potential problem will go away. Such a strategy courts epic disaster".

An Inspector can be held liable for non-compliance with federal, state, or local regulations. Consistent with the hazardous nature of asbestos, any assessment for the presence of asbestos is understood to be a critical task. Therefore, regulatory agencies on all levels have adopted diverse and explicit regulations concerning the performance of asbestos assessments.

The primary area is the compliance with Inspector certification requirements. Not only must the Inspector take an EPA approved course and pass an examination as required by the federal government, he or she must also often comply with state, county, and local regulations for certification. Other regulations that the inspector must comply with relate to the use of respirators and protective clothing while conducting an inspection.

The failure to comply with regulations can result in both fines and revocation of inspection certifications. These actions are taken by an administrative agency, such as the Environmental Protection Agency (EPA). Any arguments made by an Inspector against the administrative penalty must first be argued before a hearing officer. It is very difficult to successfully overturn an administrative penalty in an administrative hearing. Only after "exhausting administrative remedies" could an Inspector attempt to obtain relief from an administrative action by going to court.

Simply stated, failure by an Inspector to follow regulations can lead directly to administrative sanctions from a variety of government agencies. Once the sanctions are assessed, it is difficult for an Inspector to successfully overturn any administrative penalties.

CRIMINAL LIABILITY

Although remote, it is possible for an inspector to be held criminally liable. In the criminal context, it is the government that is prosecuting the action. Importantly, a criminal conviction is very serious and may involve both fines and incarceration. A criminal conviction will also result in a record.

To be held criminally responsible, the Inspector must meet two elements. First, the inspector must know his actions are wrong. Second, the inspector must perform a guilty act. An example would be the inspector who consciously failed to define the asbestos content of a material, was aware that the material was suspect, and was aware that his action would lead directly to extensive contamination and exposure. In this context, a District Attorney may choose to prosecute a criminal action.

CIVIL LIABILITY

Civil actions involve a suit by a private party against a private party. In contrast, both the Administrative and Criminal contexts involve employees of a government initiating a legal action. By far, civil liability is the greatest source of potential liability to an inspector.

Civil liability includes actions based on contractual and <u>tort</u> theories.

Contractual Liability

The inspector is liable for breach of contract if the services are not performed in accordance with the explicit and implicit meaning of the agreement. A contract need not be written to be enforceable; contracts can be oral as well as implied by a court from the behavior of the parties. If a court finds that there's mutuality of obligation, a meeting of the minds, and that the

agreement is not against public policy, the court will attempt to strictly enforce a contract. In a contract action, the court will look to the agreement to determine the intent of the parties. The court will then enforce a contract in order to avoid unjust enrichment and in an attempt to place the parties in the position they would have been in had the agreement been performed faithfully. In terms of remedies, the court will assess financial awards; it is very rare that the court will order the parties to specifically perform the agreement.

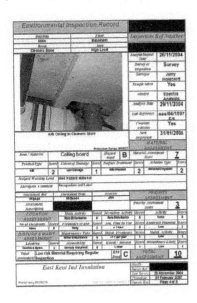

East Kent Ind Insulation

When a contract is written, the court will first decide if the written agreement was intended to embody the entire agreement. If the court decides that the contract integrates the entire agreement between the parties, the court will focus only on the language of the contract to determine the rights of the parties. In this context, any attempt by a party to contradict the explicit terms of the contract with testimony regarding oral promises or representations will fail. The court will strictly interpret the written agreement.

Contractual liability is one of the greatest sources of liability facing an Inspector. The number of contract actions is a direct result of poor drafting of both proposals and contracts. Reliance on "boilerplate" language in proposals and contracts is the single most common reason for arguments, which lead, to lawsuits alleging breach of contract. The failure to ensure a "meeting of the minds" by drafting a specific contract that defines the agreement is a recipe for legal actions.

Asbestos Inspection Report

The second most common cause of contract suits is the fact that more emphasis is placed on the price of the contract rather than the scope-of-work. By definition, a contract to perform an asbestos assessment is a contract to define an unknown: in other words, how much asbestos is present in a building. A properly performed asbestos survey will allow the conditions on-site, (i.e., the number, types and locations of suspect asbestos containing materials) to determine the scope-of-work (i.e., survey duration and number of samples). However, emphasis is placed on the price of the assessment. Many breach of contract suits result from an Inspector not being able to perform both professionally and profitably.

Perhaps the best example comes from the public bidding process where selection on the basis of price is required by procurement regulations. In schools, most inspection contracts are bid on a competitive, fixed-fee basis after the school system has presented the building plans as a basis of the bids. In this context, the price of the contract, not the number of samples necessary to professionally define all suspect materials, becomes the focus. The only way to ensure profitability is to perform the assessment with haste and limit the number of samples. Low bid leads directly to low quality. Low quality is often the basis of a breach of contract action.

Clarity in contract language is the best means of avoiding disputes. If the Inspector contracted to inspect a given number of square feet based on information provided by the building owner, the owner would pay an additional amount if the square footage estimates are inaccurate. If the inspector were to win a bid to inspect "all the buildings," the inspector would be liable for the inspection of all areas without a square footage limitation. Does this contract include roofing materials?

The timing of the completion of an inspection can be of great concern to the school and the subject of breach of contract action. If the school officials have a timetable by which they must solicit bids from contractors, the completion of the inspection becomes an important contractual consideration. Liquidated damages are often defined in the contract and are claimed against the inspector for failure to complete on time.

The extent of sampling and documentation of results are other areas in which the building owner and inspector should have a clear contractual understanding. The inspector should not enter into a contract in which an insufficient number of samples are specified so that the presence of asbestos may not be detected. The appropriate type of laboratory analysis at a certified laboratory should be specified in the contract. The building owner may save money in the short run by economizing on sampling; however, such practices could cause legal problems for both the building owner and the inspector later.

Furthermore, if the contract calls for "best practices" or state-of-the-art protocols for sampling, then provides insufficient funds for sampling, the inspector would be caught in a situation in which he could be open to (1) later litigation if there is asbestos-related damage and, (2) breach of contract action by the school or building owner.

The records turned over to the school or building owner by the inspector are the end product of the contracts. Not only should the nature and form of these records be specified, but also any special procedures to be followed in developing the set of records. Assuring the chain-of-custody of samples between the inspector and laboratory is an example of where the inspector might be personally liable to re-sample all areas of the school if proper custody procedures are not followed.

Tort Liability

A "tort" is a generic legal term for a class of theories advanced in civil litigation. Common tort theories include negligence, fraud, misrepresentation, assault, and battery.

Tort Liability and Negligence

The most common tort theory advanced against an inspector would be negligence. A negligence claim alleges that the inspector failed to perform her work in accordance with the skills of the profession. To win a negligence suit, the plaintiff must prove that the inspector failed to perform the services in a professional manner, using that degree of care and skill ordinarily exercised by and consistent with the standards of competent consultants practicing in the same or a similar locality. The plaintiff must prove each of the following items:

- Duty
  - The inspector had a duty to the plaintiff that is recognized in a court of law
- Breach of Duty
  - The Inspector's actions constituted a breach of the duty owed to the plaintiff.
- Unreasonable
  - The inspector's actions were not objectively reasonable: in other words, a "reasonable inspector" would not have performed as the inspector did. As elements of proof, state-of-the-art practices, regulatory guidance documents, and industry standards would be offered to show that the inspector's actions were unreasonable
- Injury
  - The plaintiff must show that she was "injured" by the inspectors actions. Fear of future consequences usually does not suffice; the plaintiff must show real-time injury such as clinical medical tests or the loss of a sale of real estate.
- Proximate Cause
  - The plaintiff must prove that the inspector's action was the direct cause of the injury. The two events should be connected closely in time and space.
- Damages
  - The court will award damages, in the form of monetary awards, to compensate for the injury. Some jurisdictions also allow punitive damages in addition to compensatory damages.

Negligence can arise from the inspector failing to document an area of ACM or improperly taking samples. One of the great difficulties in defining a potential liability due to negligence is the lack of universally accepted performance standards for asbestos inspection activities. Three examples will illustrate this problem.

Example A   An inspector is called upon to assess the condition of a material. A great deal of subsequent abatement activity depends on this assessment. There does not exist at present any definitive distinction between what is damaged material and what is significantly damaged material. No precise instrument measures this damage; only the inspector judges the ACM's condition. Such assessments could change from one inspector to another or may change as more is learned about the mechanism of fiber released.

17

Example B   The inspector is called upon to assess the potential damage of ACM, i.e. the *potential* of the material to release fibers in the future. The potential for damage depends upon other factors, including the activities in the areas of the ACM and the operation of the ventilation system of the school. There is no precise approach at present to such an assessment. In addition, the use of the areas may change from the time the inspector made his or her potential damage determination. The inspector can try to protect himself in the inspection contract form liability of future fiber release due to altered activity patterns in the school. The inspection contract could include a "changed conditions" or "differing site conditions" clause which provides some protection to the inspector if physical conditions occur at the site which differs from those originally observed.

Example C   Where previous inspections have been performed, before using the results, it must be determined whether the inspection was properly designed and performed and whether the inspection was performed by a person competent in this area. Reliance upon previous inspections without these confirmations may result in improper conclusions being drawn and improper responses being taken.

LEGAL CONSIDERATIONS OF INSURANCE

Obtaining professional liability insurance is the normal method for a professional, such as an Asbestos Inspector, to secure protection from litigation arising from his professional activities. These policies are often referred to as Errors and Omission (E&O) policies.

Many owners require that all professionals involved in asbestos-related work have liability insurance in order to have some financial security for significant claims that may arise. In addition, under certain state and local laws, general liability insurance in specified amounts is often required.

A related aspect of this issue is the necessity for indemnification clauses in the contract, whereby the professional is obligated to <u>indemnify</u> and defend the owner against claims brought against the owner arising out of the inspector's work. A the same time, inspectors need such insurance to protect themselves against claims which can be financial ruinous, and to provide for legal defense costs against claims. While work done in accordance with specifications and applicable regulations may ultimately shield the inspector from liability, the assumption of defense of a legal action by the insurance carrier, or the client (building owner) who indemnifies the inspector, is a significant benefit.

It is obvious that insurance adds to the inspector's cost of performance and thus is eventually paid by the owner. Complicating the asbestos management issue is the difficulty most professionals involved in asbestos are having obtaining meaningful insurance at any price. Due to the current relative unavailability of insurance, and the expense of substantive E&O policies, many owners have considered dropping or reducing insurance requirements, and sometimes are forced to do so to obtain professional services.

The relative unavailability of insurance has forced asbestos professionals in some cases to purchase any insurance available, without paying adequate attention to whether risks are covered or the strength or credibility of the carrier. Similarly, owners are accepting insurance certificates without analyzing the coverage being offered. Changes in the type and scope of coverage offered by the insurance industry must therefore be analyzed carefully to accomplish the goal of insurance. Rather than protection against liability, insurance for some has become a "license to work" in the asbestos industry.

These asbestos professionals who purchase insurance, regardless of the cost or quality of coverage, can obtain work. Others are forced to attempt to negotiate alternatives with owners to providing such insurance. However, unless the insured understand what coverage is being purchased, the insured may be left unprotected by merely buying a "license to work."

TYPES OF INSURANCE COVERAGE

Errors and Omissions

Building Inspectors will normally look for "Errors and Omissions" insurance to protect them against misjudgments made during building sections. The mistake may take the form of an inadvertent error (i.e., miscalculation of area square footage) or an unintentional omission of some nature (i.e., not enough samples collected). Errors and Omissions (E&O) coverage is written for specific professions. Many professionals  (architect, engineer, designer, etc.) have E&O coverage to protect them; however, asbestos related professionals may have difficulty obtaining full coverage due to the great exposure for loss in their activities. If errors and omissions insurance is found by the asbestos professional, the coverage might be very expensive. As of this writing it would not be uncommon for E&O to cost in the range of $40,000 as an annual premium to ensure $1,000,000 in coverage, with a $20,000 deductible, on a per occurrence basis.

19

SECTION D: LEGAL LIABILITIES OF INSPECTORS

General Liability Insurance

Another type of coverage that Building inspectors might pursue, general liability insurance, is available and may serve as protection for events that occur during building inspections. As the name implies, general liability coverage is suitable for situations arising in the normal course of business and not related to the inspector's delivery of professional options. The drawback to this type of insurance is that it will likely contain a pollution or asbestos exclusion, rendering the policy essentially ineffective for asbestos-related claims.

Occurrence Insurance

In the past, liability insurance has been written on an "occurrence" basis. Under such a policy, if an incident "occurs" while the policy is in force, coverage is afforded even if the actually claim is made some years later and even if the insured is no longer insured by the same carrier. As a result of this type of coverage, insurance carriers must defend claims brought years after companies are no longer insurance by the carrier. With the long latency period of asbestos related disease, occurrence coverage can result in great losses to carriers who have not received premiums over a period of time. As a result, the carriers have been adding exclusions to existing policies for asbestos related third-party claims and generally have changed the coverage from occurrence to "claims made."

Claims Made Insurance

Under a "claims made" policy, coverage exists if a claim is made while the policy is in force. In certain situations, a claim may be made during an extended reporting period ("tail"), which may require an additional premium. For many risks, the difference between occurrence and claims made coverage is not significant since the liability causing event is obvious and claims
are generally asserted shortly after the event occurs. However, the release of asbestos fibers form an asbestos abatement project may not be obvious, and injury may not be detected for twenty years. Thus, if claims made coverage is obtained, it may not be of value in such cases if (1) the insured changes insurance carriers before a claim is made, (2) the carrier terminates coverage under a policy, or (3) the carrier withdraws from the market before a claim is filed. Nevertheless, it is likely that the primary type of coverage to be available in the future is claims made, and thus another analysis must be made by the inspector to understand the coverage that is actually being purchased.

There is no single definition of what "claims made" means; it is mandatory that the insured read and understand the coverage provided under its policy. All exclusions, conditions, and definitions must be carefully analyzed. For example, a general liability policy written for an asbestos contractor often includes a "pollution exclusion." This excludes coverage for any personal injury or property damage caused by a broad list of substances. Generally, asbestos is included on the list and consequently the policy provides no coverage for asbestos risks.

There are several important considerations in making an analysis of available insurance coverage or in specifying the same:

1. True "occurrence" coverage is rare. The terms of the policy must be reviewed carefully. Some "occurrence" policies have conditions or exclusions that negate coverage. The name of the policy makes no difference. Claims made policies may, in some situations, cover claims which arose in prior years, similar to "occurrence" policies.
2. The insurance certificate provides little or no information of benefit to an owner or professional consultant. The policy itself must be reviewed.
3. The insurance carrier must be carefully evaluated. Does the carrier understand the industry, and is it committed to writing proper coverage? Again, the policy terms are important.

BONDING

The difficulties in obtaining insurance have spread to the bonding industry. Traditionally, two types of bonds have been required in the construction industry to protect the owner or lender against the contractor's financial default:

- Payment bonds, under which a surety company agrees to pay for labor and materials supplied to project in the event the contractor fails to do so; and
- Performance bonds, under which a surety agrees to complete performance of a project if the contractor fails to do so.

Abatement contractors who have had their insurance cancelled or not renewed are experiencing difficulties in obtaining bonding. Bonding companies rely on the financial ability of the principal (the contractor) to respond to claims under payment and performance bonds. If a company is not insured against catastrophic liability, the financial underpinnings of the company are weakened, and the bonding company becomes apprehensive over issuing bonds. In a similar vein, lenders are reacting adversely to the no insurance/no bonding problems of such companies. Lenders are advising companies who find themselves in such positions that lines of credit will not be renewed, for the same given by the bonding companies.

The difficulty being encountered by asbestos abatement contractors in obtaining bonding is severe. For reasons similar to those which caused the asbestos abatement insurance crisis, many contractors are unable to obtain sufficient bonding and, in some cases, any bonding. In addition to the general underwriting concerns about the contractor's ability to perform the work, another reason some bonding companies are unwilling to write bonds for asbestos abatement work relates directly to liability insurance problems. Because the bonding contract often has requirements for the contractor to obtain and maintain certain liability insurance coverage on the project, the bonding companies fear that if the contractor had insurance problems, such as improper coverage or cancellation during the policy period, the potential loss that may otherwise be covered by liability insurance might be covered by the contractor's performance bond.

While the traditional concepts of bond underwriting may not be applicable to abatement contractors, it is nevertheless useful to understand them. The primary considerations of the bonding company in determining whether to bond a contractor are the ability of the contractor to perform the work and the contractor's financial ability. A proven track record of successfully completed projects, without ensuing litigation, is very helpful to the contractor in demonstrating to the bonding company its ability to perform the work. Financial stability is important not only with respect to the contractor's ability to perform the work, but also its ability to satisfy its indemnity obligation to the bonding company in the even a loss is suffered under the bonds. Unlike insurance, a payment or performance bond gives the bonding company the right to recover back against the contract for any losses sustained by it under the bond. A somewhat more intangible, yet important, factor is the contractor's good character. Despite satisfactorily proving all of these items, a contractor may still not be able to obtain sufficient bonding in today's market. In such events, an owner may waive or refuse bonding requirements or arrange other contractual mechanisms to assure payment or performance.

There are numerous legal considerations involved in the evaluation of insurance and bonding coverage. The cost of insurance for asbestos abatement is significant, and if such expense is going to be undertaken, the coverage obtained should be satisfactory. While there are no easy solutions in the decision-making process, it is mandatory that contractors, consultants, and owners undertake to become knowledgeable purchasers of insurance

The shift in types of coverage written for the contracting industry from occurrence to claims made, and the difficulty in obtaining bonds have placed greater emphasis on the contractor's commitment to the performance of work in a quality manner, the carrier's commitment to continuing to insure asbestos abatement contractors, and the quality of the carrier's coverage and insurance program in general. This makes the process of purchasing insurance more complicated, but thorough review of the considerations outlined above will greatly assist the contractor, consultant, or owner in making a knowledgeable choice.

Ever since the discovery of the dangerous nature of asbestos back in the 1920's, US employers have regularly been in trouble for negligence shown to their employees. In total, around 5,000 court cases have been filed and won as a result of direct asbestos exposure - with a further 15,000 cases being settled outside of the court room (probably more, but statistics show 15,000). Thus, the history of the asbestos / health issue is lengthy. If you are currently considering taking legal action against your employer due to their negligence of workplace laws - here is a bit of information to back up your case.

You ultimately need to understand that you are not alone, and that many people have suffered in similar ways to you in the past. While compensation can't bring back good health - it can certainly relieve the pain of high medical bills and debilitating time off work.

INTRODUCTION

A person inspecting a facility for ACM should understand the interrelationships among building systems, recognize where asbestos is likely to be found, and be familiar with blueprints and other resource material which may be available for his or her use. Knowledge of how buildings are constructed and operated is vital to conducting a thorough building survey for ACBM.

THE INTERRELATIONSHIPS OF BUILDING SYSTEMS

Each building is a combination of four basic building systems. These systems are generally labeled for engineering discipline responsible for their design and drafting.

The architect is the design professional who has overall responsibility for the project. The architect will hire consultants-electrical, mechanical, and structural engineers- to bring specific knowledge to the design team. In addition, other consultants (e.g. acoustical engineers, interior designers, kitchen consultants, etc.) may be employed if the specific project warrants.

The structural system is the skeleton of the building and consists of beams, columns, bearing walls, and foundations which support the loads of the building and its occupants. The <u>mechanical systems</u> are the <u>heating, ventilating, and air conditioning</u> (HVAC) and the <u>plumbing systems</u> of the building. The <u>electrical systems</u> are the power and lighting systems of the building.

To provide a complete building, all of these systems must meld into a coherent and consistent facility. The architect's responsibilities are to coordinate these systems, and to choose the exterior and interior finishes and materials which are not part of the above described engineering systems.

PHYSICAL PLAN LAYOUT

When designing a building, the design team is typically faced with limitations, notably occupant and functional requirements, a budget, and building code regulations. Consequently the physical layout of the buildings can be very simple, with the structural systems being repetitive and the mechanical and electrical systems being served with minimal runs of ducts, piping, and conduit.

In multi-story buildings, the systems are simplified vertically. Generally, a utility core runs vertically through the building. From this core, service runs branch to individual floors. Elevators are generally bundled, and stair towers run vertically through the structure. Although this vertical utility core can be difficult to access, it should always be inspected for suspect ACBM.

The structural system is aligned vertically to simplify the skeletal frame By simplifying the physical plan layout, the design team is able to achieve greater benefit within the restrictions placed upon the project. High rise structural steel frame buildings nearly always contain spray-applied fireproofing. In such structures built before 1973, this spray-applied fireproofing is highly suspect of ACBM.

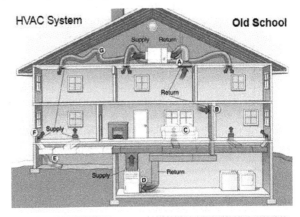

MECHANICAL SYSTEMS

Mechanical systems are those systems designed by the mechanical engineer. They include the HVAC system, the plumbing system, and in selected regions of the U.S., elevators.

Heating, Ventilating, and Air Conditioning (HVAC) Systems

SYSTEM COMPONENTS	WHAT'S WRONG WITH THIS SYSTEM?
A: Attic System Return Air	1. No Stale Air Exhaust
B: Basement System Return Air	2. No Fresh Air Feed
C: Exterior Wall Supply Air	3. No Energy Recovery Ventilation (ERV)
D: Return Air Filter	4. No Humidy Control
E: Crawlspace Insulated Duct	5. No Air Purification System
F: Supply Air Outlets	6. No Passive Heat or Air Circulation
G: Attic Supply Ducts	*Oversize mechanical system and massive ductwork*

Individual spaces or zones in a building are served by supply and return air and a thermostat to control the HVAC system. The supply and return may be in ductwork or in a plenum. Plenums are spaces, for example, the space above a dropped acoustical ceiling and below the roof or floor above. In most cases, the plenum is used for return air, that is, the air leaves the room, enters the plenum, and is drawn into the mechanical room from the plenum.

All HVAC systems consist of a means of heat transfer. The heat transfer may occur in the central mechanical space or "plant," but in large buildings or complexes it will occur in individual mechanical rooms. From the mechanical room the supply is sent to individual spaces within the building, the return air is carried back to the mechanical room where it is filtered and re-conditioned. In addition, some make-up air is added from the outside to augment any air lost through the opening of doors and windows and to provide a source of fresh air to the building.

Heating and/or cooling of indoor air are both called air conditioning. For this reason you are likely to find "Air Conditioning Plans" included in the sets of working drawings for both heating and cooling systems.

By the engineering definition, heat transfer only occurs when a warmer object gives up some of its heat to a cooler object. Exactly how the transfer occurs is dependent upon the system being used. HVAC systems can be classified as follows:

- Air Systems
  - There are two types of air HVAC systems—single duct and double duct. (This refers to supply only; return is accomplished in yet another duct.) A single duct system delivers either heated or cooled air at a constant temperature from the air conditioning equipment through ductwork. Often, a variable air volume system is used, wherein the air conditioning requirements of a space activate a damper that controls air flow based on those requirements. A terminal reheat unit, located near the point of discharge, may also be used to boos heating. When a double duct system is used, one duct carries cooled air while the other carries heated air. The two ducts meet at a mixing box, where the amount of heated or cooled air is regulated based on the requirements of the space(s) being served.
- Water Systems
  - Heated and/or cooled water is delivered to a fan coil unit, where the air is introduced. Air is blown across coils as regulated by dampers, again activated by the requirement of the space. This air is introduced through a separate duct system from the mechanical or fan room, or from a direct connection to the outside, or may simply be ambient room air
  - Water systems are either two or four pipe systems. A two pipe system has a single supply and single return pipe (thus the two pipes). With two pipes it is possible to either heat or cool at any given time, but not both at the same time. However, floors with mixed occupancy or exposure to more than one point of the compass often require heating and cooling at the same time. Conversion of a two pipe system to the heating or cooling cycle requires a shut down and conversion of the system. This takes a matter of hours, and thus cannot be accomplished in those days where it would be beneficial to heat in the morning and cool in the afternoon.
  - A four pip system delivers both heated and cooled water (called "chilled water" as it is supplied by a chiller) at the same time. Two pipes supply and return heated water, and the other two pipes supply and return chilled water. The heat transfer coil may then call for whichever water supply is required to meet the space needs.

26

- Refrigerant Systems
    - These are normally pre-packaged units that supply heating or cooling directly to a space through a wall or roof. In general, these are used only in specialized installations in commercial buildings.
- Radiant Systems
    - Radiant systems include any number of devices which are either embedded in the wall or floor assembly, or are set as radiators, usually along an exterior wall. They are usually used for heating and function by radiating heat directly into a space. That is, no air is blown across the heat transfer surface.

The precise HVAC system layout and distribution is a product of the architectural design and engineering analysis of each individual building.

Since the primary function of the HVAC system is to heat and cool building spaces, insulation is used to inhibit unwanted heat transfer. Insulation is typically found on the outside of boilers (block, blanket, or board insulation) and on the breeching or flue which conveys waste gases from the combustion process. Blanket or batt insulation is sometimes found inside ducts, and insulation is sometimes sprayed on the outside of ducts. Each of these types of insulation should be considered suspect. In addition, gasket material on boiler doors, rope used as filler in openings, valve packing, fire stop packing, and vibration-dampening cloth connecting sections of ductwork may contain asbestos. Pipe insulation is discussed below.

HVAC systems which use chilled water will typically include a cooling tower where excess heat is rejected to outdoor air. (The chilled water does not pass through the cooling tower, but rather tower water from the chiller passes through the tower.)

A typical house plumbing system

PLUMBING SYSTEMS

Plumbing systems include any water, gas or other fluid which is piped through a building, and in some cases disposed of as waste. Also considered part of the plumbing system is air when used in a non-HVAC manner, such as compressed air in hospitals, factories, or manufacturing facilities.

Plumbing systems consist of piping (horizontal pipes are called runs, vertical pipes are called risers). Other components may include valves, elbows, fittings, joints, etc.

The water systems in a building are of four types: consumed, circulated, static, and controlled. The consumed system is potable water for use and consumption by building occupants. This is also referred to as "domestic water". Circulated water is water which is circulated form a "plant" to the HVAC equipment in a two or four pipe system, as described above. Static water is water used for fire protection, and controlled water is water used to maintain relative humidity within the building.

The use of asbestos in plumbing systems is usually for the purpose of temperature control. Generally it can be found on the piping and equipment which heat water and/or maintain water at a stable temperature. Insulating materials prevent heat loss from hot pipes and equipment and water condensation on the outside of cold pipes and equipment. Thus, insulting ACM is typically limited to consumed domestic and circulated water systems.

In the consumed water system, domestic hot water (DHW) will be insulated to limit heat loss from the point of origin to the point of use. In large building complexes, a single water heater may be installed and a recirculating system will be operated to continually circulate the water from the heater to the points of use. This arrangement saves the user the inconvenience of having to wait for the hot water to arrive from the remote source. Anticipated asbestos use in these installations will be the insulation in and around the water heater and the insulation on the piping throughout the building.

In the circulated water system, heating water (HW) and chilled water (CW) are circulated from the boiler and chiller to the air handling units (AHU) in various parts of the building. The temperature at which the HW and CW arrive in the AHUs directly affects the potential of heat transfer. To maintain the temperature from the source to the point of use, insulation is required along the entire pipe runs. The insulation may contain asbestos.

In addition to plumbing insulation, asbestos cement pipe may have been used in the plumbing systems, waste systems, and roof drains. The pipe is concrete-like in appearance and known by the trade name "Transite[TM]."

ELECTRICAL SYSTEMS

Electrical systems within a building may appear very complex, but are simple in their basic design. Each building includes a primary electric service entrance; the point where the energy enters the building. This is where the meter is located.

In large buildings, transformers will be set on site to reduce the high voltage supply from the electric company to the lower voltage used within the building. In smaller buildings, the transformer will be outside the building, either on a pad or on a pole. Once the voltage has been reduced, the service is then divided into individual circuits. The size and capacity of each circuit is based on the anticipated energy requirements of items served by that circuit. The division into circuits occurs at a panel(s).

Asbestos use in electrical systems has included:
- Asbestos-cement ducts for electrical cable runs
- Partitions in electrical panels
- Asbestos cloth to bind bare cables
- Insulation on stage lighting and on wire to those lights

Of great concern in inspecting electrical systems is the potential hazard to the inspector from unsafe inspection procedures. Some guidelines for work in and around electric equipment include:
- Whenever possible, conduct the inspection accompanied by a building operator (specifically an electrician, if possible) who is familiar with the electrical equipment , its operation, and location.
- Look for and heed any "Danger High Voltage" signs.
- Ask that the system be deenergized before taking samples.
- Use extreme care not to cut into or through cables or cable insulation.
- Be wary of electrical insulation which can flake off with time and heat.
- Beware of exposed electrical wires and components.
- Do not sue a wetting solution near an electrical system.
- When taking samples of surfacing or other suspect materials, be careful not to penetrate to electrical components that may be located underneath or behind. Unless electrical power can be shut off, it may be best to assume certain electrical components to be ACBM.

CONTRACT DOCUMENTS

Contract documents or construction documents are the legally binding drawings and specifications which are used to construct the building. They consist of:
- Working Drawings
- Specifications
- Other documents including general and supplementary conditions, general requirements, agreement, addenda, and change orders.

These documents are a rich source of information for Building inspectors. Building owners should be able to provide copies. If they are not available, check with the local building permit agency. If the jurisdiction has a plan check and building permit procedure, the plan check agency likely retained a set of the drawings. These drawings are often photographically reduced and stores, but even in that form, they should be valuable documents for the inspector.

SECTION E: UNDERSTANDING BUILDING SYSTEMS

WORKING DRAWINGS

The working drawings or plans are a set of drawings which indicate the finished appearance and construction of the building. They are not a set of exact instructions for the contractor. As such, they do not precisely reflect the building as it was constructed. For this reason, it is mandatory that all information gathered from the plans be verified.

A title block will appear along the right side or in the lower right hand corner of each sheet of the set of drawings. When beginning your review of the drawings, carefully examine the title block for the following information:
- The name of the project (i.e., original construction vs. any kind of renovation)
- The name of the architectural or engineering firm
- The date of the drawings
- The sheet numbers
- The project number

Compare the sheet numbering to the Index of Drawings on the cover sheet to determine (1) that you have a complete set, and (2) that all the sheets have the same date. The project number and date are your clues to whether you are reviewing plans for the same project. Over the life span of a building several renovation projects are likely to have been completed. An inspector will want to systematically review the set of drawings for each project individually.

The sheet numbering system for the entire set of drawings reflects the manner in which the drawings were prepared. just as the design of the building is a collaborative effort of an architect and engineers, the drawings and specifications are prepared by each of these professionals. Altogether, a complete set of drawings will likely include:
- Civin
- Architectural
- Structural
- Mechanical (HVAC)
- Plumbing
- Electrical

When examining the numbering of the drawings, you will find that the drawings are divided by discipline. That is, the architectural drawings are together, the structural drawings are together, and so on. The numbering is then dependent on the discipline. It is typical that the structural drawings will be identified with an S and then the sheet number, e.g. S-1, S-2, S-3. Architectural drawings will be identified with an A, civil drawings with a C, the mechanical (HVAC) with an M, the plumbing with a P, and the electrical with an E. Miscellaneous other drawings may include landscaping (L), fire protection (FP), etc.

Regrettably, there is no standardization in the production of drawings, and thus no set of rules can be given for the way that each architect or engineer prepares not only a set of drawings but also individual items within that set. You may even find inconsistencies within a particular set of drawings, as the drawings are developed by different people in different offices.

Drawings can be divided into several generic types:
- Floor plans-drawings of the building as viewed from above, these include floor plans, foundation plans, framing plans, roof plans, electrical plans, and should not be confused with the entire set of drawings which is also referred to as the "set of plans"; (See Exhibit E-1)
- Elevations-generally drawings of the building as viewed horizontally from outside; these can also be elevations of interior components or finished; (See Exhibit E-2)
- Sections-drawings cut (vertically) through the building or building parts; (See Exhibit E-3)
- Details-expanded views of small areas that can be drawn in plan, elevation, or section; (See Exhibit E-4)
- Notes, symbols, legends, abbreviations-comments and explanations; (See Exhibit E-5)
- Schedules-a tabular display of information; (i.e., door schedule, room finish schedule, mechanical equipment schedule, etc.) (See Exhibit E-6)

As you review the drawings be sure to check for a list of symbols. Each building material in a set of drawings is depicted, when cut in section, by a material indication. If a legend appears in the set, use it as your guide. If no legend appears, refer to the legend in Exhibit E-7, but verify based on a visit to the site. Use this legend with caution-it is only a guide as there is no standardization of material and equipment symbols.

Symbols are also used for a variety of items on drawings, other than materials. These are called reference symbols. Again, if a legend is included in the set of drawings use it, if not, then use the reference symbol legend indicated in Exhibit E-8 as a guide.

A drawing reference that you may encounter on a set of building plans is a "revision". It is depicted by a triangle around a number; a portion of the drawing itself may be "clouded" to further indicate where the revision applies (See Exhibit E-8). The number identifies the revision. The key to the numbering is found in the area adjacent to the title block. Revisions can be added to the drawings when changes have occurred:
- After the drawings have been issued for bid
- As a result of the plan check/permitting process

ARCHITECTURAL DRAWINGS

Architectural drawings show finished surfaces and materials. Of note is the floor plan, which is cut horizontally through the building at about four feet above the floor. The floor plan is the basis for mechanical, plumbing, and electrical drawings.

Another important drawing in the demolition plan, which represents those portions of the building which will be demolished as a part of the renovation project. In many projects, improvements include removing (demolishing) existing walls, replacing floor coverings, and other changes. The existing walls, windows, doors, and built-ins are all indicated much lighter in contrast to the area to be demolished. The difference in thickness of lines on the drawing signals the areas where work is to occur.

Commercial buildings often have repetitive units-rooms, doors, and windows. To organize these spaces, schedules are developed to identify and describe specific rooms, doors, and windows. The specific item is referenced to the schedule with a symbol as shown on the legend in the set of drawings. If a legend does not accompany the drawings, refer to Exhibit E-8, as a guide for typical symbols used. Use extreme care when working with room, door, and window designations as the same number may be used repeatedly, and the only difference will be in the symbol in which the number is lettered.

Be aware of differences between the room numbering scheme in the plans and the current numbering of the rooms in the building. IT may be necessary to cross-list the numbers to equate the design information with the information determined from on-site investigation.

The room finish schedule will guide the inspector through the finishes, or surface treatments, used in the individual rooms. The schedules read like a graph with columns title-floors, base, wainscot, walls, and ceilings. Any changes may be an indication of prior renovation that may have added ACBM.

When reviewing drawings, your intention should be to familiarize yourself with the layout of the building, and then examine in detail the finishes, or details at the exterior wall and other areas where you suspect ACM may be found.

Often, when referenced on the drawings, a material will be listed with the notation "OR EQUAL". This notation allows from the contractor to make a substitution of another equivalent material. The determination of what is equal is usually at the architect's or engineer's discretion, as elaborated upon in specifications. This determination is based on descriptive literature forwarded by the

contractor, for the architect's or engineer's review and owner's approval; usually by charge order.

STRUCTURAL DRAWINGS

Structural drawings will consist of foundation plans, floor framing plans, roof framing plans, structural elevations, details, notes, and schedules. All structural drawings are drawn without finish (architectural) materials or other engineering systems, and are intended only to indicate the structural elements of the building.
When you review the structural drawings, you will need to be familiar with the building in general, and in particular with <u>structural members</u>-beams, columns, and slabs.

Many buildings use a structural grid (see Exhibit E-9), referenced by numbers or letters at the building's column lines. The grid provides a way to organize the building and to communicate about specific areas.

If the building has fireproofing, it may not be indicated on the structural drawings as it is a finish or surfacing specified by the architect usually, to be applied to the skeleton, not part of the skeleton. Thus it is the architect's responsibility not the structural engineer's However, to understand where the fireproofing has been applied, where the beams are located that it is applied to, and the amount of area covered, the inspector will need to examine the structural drawings. Exhibit E-10 illustrates different substrates and various ways fireproofing is applied.

Structural notes will often include a building code reference. These codes identify the name and year of the official building code(s)-city, county, or state-which governed the design of the structural elements. This reference can be an invaluable tool. Building codes in effect when the building was erected may have specified fireproofing and other materials which are likely to contain asbestos.

MECHANICAL DRAWINGS

The mechanical engineer prepares drawings for both the HVAC system and the plumbing system. Mechanical drawings consist of mechanical plans, which are based on the building's floor plans. They indicate the routing of ductwork and piping systems (necessary for HVAC), and well as details, notes, schedules, sections, and elevations (if required). Mechanical plans may include a system schematic, or flow diagram, to indicate how the HVAC system operates.

When reviewing the mechanical drawings, the inspector needs to become familiar with the kind of HVAC system used, and that evocation of the various parts of the system. It is necessary to verify information obtained from these drawings by field inspection.

33

PLUMBING DRAWINGS

Plumbing drawings include plumbing plans, which are based on floor plans, notes, schedules, rise diagrams, and other required supporting drawings.

When reviewing the plumbing drawings, you need to be concerned with where the various equipment is located, how the system works, and whether the information on the plans is verified upon inspection. Be alert to pipe chases, utility cores or tunnels, or other inaccessible spaces that may enclose ACBM.

ELECTRICAL DRAWINGS

Electrical drawings consist of the floor plan-based power and lighting plans, notes, schedules, details (if required) and calculations to support the load requirements. A cursory review of the electrical drawings, is normally all that is required to familiarize yourself with the location of equipment and equipment rooms. Electrical drawings are largely schematic. The exact location of all items, excepting panels, lighting, switches and receptacles, is determined in the field, and as such needs to be verified by a site visit.

SPECIFICATIONS

The specifications (specs) for a project are a written set of standards and procedures which inform the contractor of what materials and standards are required for the successful completion of the facility. The specs are generally in book form and accompany the drawings as a portion of the contract documents. Just as various members of the design team are responsible for portions of the drawings, they are responsible for the corresponding portions of the specs.

Typically the drawings and specs are prepared simultaneously by different personnel in the architect's or engineer's office. It is likely that some conflict between the two may occur. If that is the case, the specs take precedence over the plans.

Specifications are either proprietary or non-proprietary. Exhibit E-11, illustrates both types of specs. Proprietary specifications require the use of a specific material from a specific manufacturer. Exhibit E-12 is a representative list of generic types of materials which may contain asbestos. Exhibit E-13 identifies trade names of materials that are known or have been inferred to contain asbestos. Non-proprietary specs do not specify a particular manufacturer, but indicate the materials or performance requirements of the material and/or equipment and allow for the selection of any number of materials or equipment which can perform to those limits. Typically, governmental projects require non-proprietary specifications as way of ensuring that one manufacturer is not given unfair advantage in pursuing a project.

As a way to organize specifications, many firms use the Construction Specifications Institute (CSI) Masterformat. The divisions of the CSI are illustrated in Exhibit E-14. Note that plumbing and HVAC are both included under division 15, "mechanical". This deviates from the separate manner in which they are treated in working drawings. However, plumbing and HVAC have specific subdivisions under division 15.

ADDENDA

Upon completion of the plans and specs, and upon authorization by the owner, the bidding period begins. During this period contractors estimate the cost of performing the work in the hope of being awarded the contract. If changes need to be made to the plans and specs each potential bidder is notified of those changes to ensure that they are all operating with the same information. This is done through issuing an addendum to the plans and specs.

And addendum may include both drawings and specifications and is legally incorporated into the contract documents. ON a complex project it is very likely that a number of addenda will be issued during the bid period. Addenda should be treated as updates to the plans.

The bid period culminates with each bidding contractor submitting its bid to the owner, followed by a bid opening. The most responsible bidder, with the most responsive bed, is accepted and a contract for the construct ion of the project is signed. The working drawings, specifications, and addenda are all incorporated into the contract. The cost and time of construction are based on these documents.

CHANGE ORDERS

A change order is a change to the documents after a contract for construction has been signed. A change order may include both drawings and specifications to illustrate the change. It is signed by the owner, architect, and contractor as a legal change to the construction contract. These items need to be consulted when investigating the building. A change order can be additive, deductive, or no cost, and can modify the schedule.

SHOP DRAWINGS AND SUBMITTALS

During the course of construction, detailed drawings or descriptions of certain items are needed before they are installed in the building. These items are as called for in the specifications Shop drawings and/or submittals (drawings or descriptive literature), are prepared by the contractor or his or her subcontractors or vendors and are reviewed by the architect and/or his or her appropriate consulting engineers. If these are available to the inspector, they can reveal significant information about equipment (mechanical and electrical) and may disclose the use of ACM.

Other forms of submittals are operating manuals and brochures which are transmitted to the owner after construction. These too may indicate materials containing asbestos. When available, they are good resource for information on suspect materials.

RECORD DOCUMENTS

As noted above, numerous changes can be made to a set of construction documents during bidding and construction. Because initial plans and specs are not exact instructions, they may be substantially changed by the time construction is completed. Drawings and specs which reflect the way a building was actually constructed are known as "record documents". Building owners should have a set of plans and specs which accurately represent their facility. Plans and specs often contain a provision for as-built drawings and specs to be delivered to the owner, by the contractor, upon completion of construction.

Record documents reflect the construction on the date produced and are, in part, outdated as soon as any modification, renovation, or remodeling occurs. Unfortunately, it is rare building owner who has accurate records of all construction data which are kept updated throughout the life of the building. Inspectors should verify the accuracy of the resource material in the field.

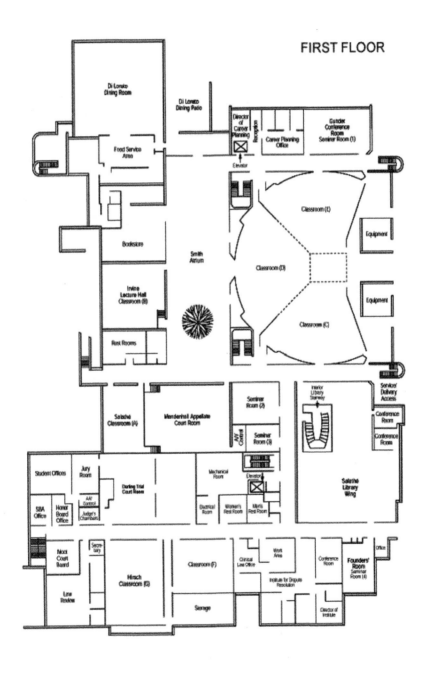

FIRST FLOOR

EXHIBIT E-1
EXAMPLE FLOOR PLAN

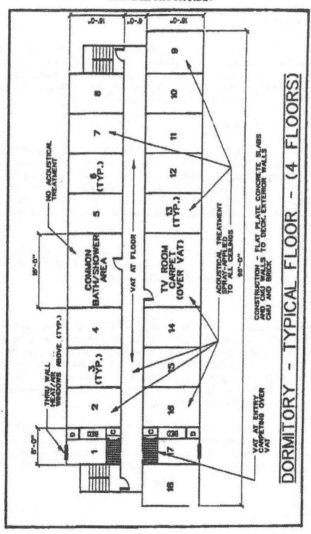

DORMITORY – TYPICAL FLOOR – (4 FLOORS)

EXHIBIT E-2
EXAMPLE OF ELEVATION DRAWING

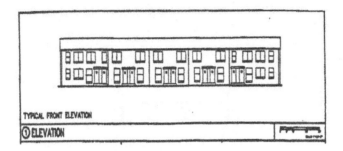

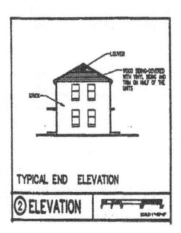

EXHIBIT E-3
EXAMPLE OF A SECTION DRAWING

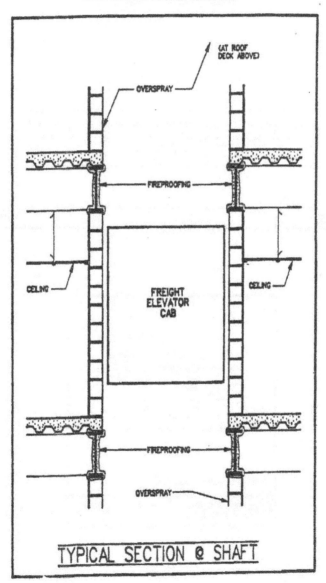

TYPICAL SECTION @ SHAFT

EXHIBIT E-4
EXAMPLE OF A DETAIL DRAWING

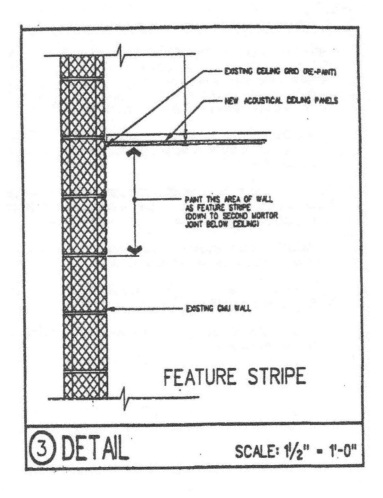

EXISTING CEILING GRID (RE-PAINT)

NEW ACOUSTICAL CEILING PANELS

PAINT THIS AREA OF WALL
AS FEATURE STRIPE
(DOWN TO SECOND MORTOR
JOINT BELOW CEILING)

EXISTING CMU WALL

FEATURE STRIPE

③ DETAIL   SCALE: 1½" = 1'-0"

EXHIBIT E-5
EXAMPLE OF DRAWINGS NOTES

General Notes

1. Perform work as required for proper completion of the job. Drawings do not propose to show all existing items or conditions. Contractor shall not receive extra payment for requirements which can be inferred through observation of existing conditions at the site. In the event concealed conditions are encountered which may vary significiantly from those indicated on the drawings, notify the architect before proceeding with work.

2. All dimensions are locations shall be checked and verified by the contractor on site and the architect shall be notified of any deviations from these drawings prior to commencement of work.

3. Any fixture substitutions shall be appproved by architect prior to installation. Contractor to submit for architect's approval, complete photometric data and pre-wired 120 volt operating sample of any proposed substitution.

4. Overloads which may result from new fixture reconnections to be checked by contractor. If overload is found, notify architect before proceeding with work.

5. Any circuit with no load due to work from this contract shall be disconnected at breaker and all unused wiring to be removed..

6. All conduit penetrations through firewall to be enclosed with approved fire stops to maintain rated fire separation of existing wall.

EXHIBIT E-6
EXAMPLE OF MASTER SCHEDULE
(for Selection/Design/Bid-Award/Construction)

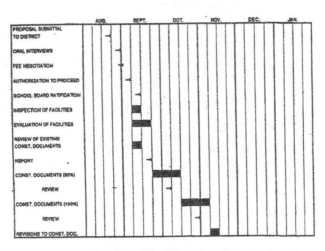

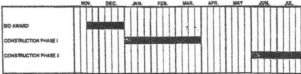

EXHIBIT E-7
MATERIAL INDICATIONS

ACOUSTICAL TILE

BRICK

CONCRETE

CMU (CONC. MASONRY UNITS)

INSULATION, LOOSE OR BATT.

INSULATION, RIGID

METAL

WOOD, FINISH

WOOD, ROUGH

PLYWOOD

CERAMIC TILE

GLASS

RESILIENT FLOOR TILE

PLASTER

GYPSUM WALL BOARD

ROCK

STONE, GRAVEL, POROUS FILL

METAL LATH AND PLASTER

STRUCTURAL CLAY TILE

EXHIBIT E-8
REFERENCE SYMBOLS

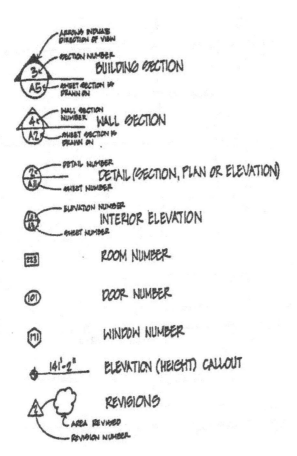

BUILDING SECTION

WALL SECTION

DETAIL (SECTION, PLAN OR ELEVATION)

INTERIOR ELEVATION

ROOM NUMBER

DOOR NUMBER

WINDOW NUMBER

ELEVATION (HEIGHT) CALLOUT

REVISIONS

EXHIBIT E-9
STRUCTURAL GRID

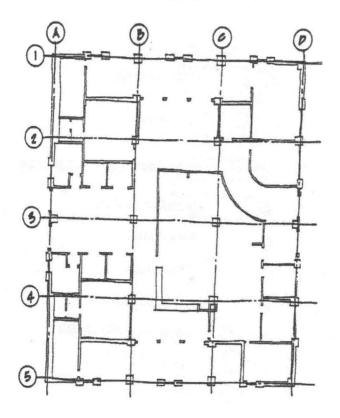

EXHIBIT E-10
TYPES OF CEILING CONSTRUCTION

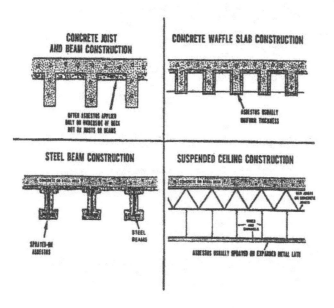

CONCRETE JOIST AND BEAM CONSTRUCTION

OFTEN ASBESTOS APPLIED ONLY ON UNDERSIDE OF DECK NOT ON JOISTS OR BEAMS

CONCRETE WAFFLE SLAB CONSTRUCTION

ASBESTOS USUALLY UNIFORM THICKNESS

STEEL BEAM CONSTRUCTION

SPRAYED-ON ASBESTOS

STEEL BEAMS

SUSPENDED CEILING CONSTRUCTION

ASBESTOS USUALLY SPRAYED ON EXPANDED METAL LATH

47

EXHIBIT E-11
SPECIFICATIONS

Proprietary

"...starting at the low edge apply on 18" wide, then over that one full 36" wide JM [Johns-Manville] Asbestos Finishing Felt."

Non-Proprietary

"Asphalt Saturated Asbestos Felt shall be 15 pounds perforated complying with ASTM Designation D 250 latest edition."

Proprietary

"Insulation shall be Pyrospray Type T, by Baldwin-Ehret-Hill, Inc; Asbestospray by Asbestospray Corporation; Sealspary by Sealtite Insulation Manufacturing Corp., Waukesha, Wisconsin; Spray Craft, Type S by Smith and Kanzler Company; or Spraydon Standard by Spraydon Research Corporation."

Non-Proprietary

"Insulation shall be a quality controlled mixture of virgin asbestos fibers and mineral wool fibers blended with inorganic binders and rust inhibitors. Binder, after setting, must be unaffected by water, moisture, and condensation."

EXHIBIT E-12
REPRESENTATIVE LIST OF MATERIALS
LIKELY TO CONTAIN ASBESTOS

The following list of materials likely to contain asbestos is by no means all inclusive. Materials not appearing on the list, in some cases, may also be considered suspect, and should be treated according to applicable regulations and good work practices. Conversely, many materials which appear on the list are currently made with non-asbestos materials.

KEY TO ABBREVIATIONS FOR EXHIBIT E-12

Material Types:

M	=	Miscellaneous Material
S	=	Surfacing Material
TSI	=	Thermal System Insulation

Plans:

Which drawings to reference for material location

A	=	Architectural Drawings
M	=	Mechanical Drawings
P	=	Plumbing Plans
E	=	Electrical Plans

Specs:

Which division used from uniform Construction Index (EXHIBIT E-14) Numbers 6-16

EXHIBIT E-12 (cont.)

SUSPECT MATERIALS	MTRL TYPES	PLANS	SPECS
Cement Asbestos Insulating Panels	M	A	6
Cement Asbestos Wallboard	M	A	6
Cement Asbestos Siding	M	A	6
Roofing, Asphalt Saturated Asbestos Felt	M	A	7
Roofing, Reinforced Asbestos Flashing Sheet	M	A	7
Roofing, Asbestos Base Felt	M	A	7
Roofing, Asbestos Finishing Felt	M	A	7
Roof, Paint	S	A	7
Roofing, Flashing (tar and felt)	M	A	7
Roofing, Flashing (plastic cement for sheet metal work)	M	A	7
Waterproofing, Asbestos Base Felt	M	A	7
Waterproofing, Asbestos Finishing Felt	M	A	7
Waterproofing, Flashing	M	A	7
Dampproofing	M	A	7
Putty and/or Caulk	M	A	7/9
Door Insulation	M	A	8
Flooring, Asphalt Tile	M	A	9
Flooring, Vinyl Asbestos Tile	M	A	9
Flooring, Vinyl Sheet	M	A	9
Flooring, Backing	M	A	9
Plaster, Acoustical or Decorative	S	A	9
Ceiling Tile	M	A	9
Insulation, Thermal Sprayed-on	S	A	9
Blown-in Insulation	M	A	9
Insulation, Fireproofing	S	A	9
Taping Compounds	S	A	9

EXHIBIT E-12 (cont.)

SUSPECT MATERIALS (continued)	MTRL TYPES	PLANS	SPECS
Paints	S	A	9
Textured Coatings	S	A	9
Packing or rope (at penetrations through floors or walls)	M	A	9
Laboratory Hoods	M	A	11
Laboratory Oven Gaskets	M	A	11
Laboratory Gloves	M	A	11
Laboratory Bench Tops	M	A	11
Fire Curtains	M	A	12
Elevators, Equipment Panels	M	A	14
Elevators, Brake Shoes	M	A	14
Elevators, Vinyl Asbestos Tile	M	A	14
HVAC Piping Insulation	TSI	M	15
HVAC Gaskets	TSI	M	15
Boiler Block or Wearing Surface	TSI	M	15
Breeching Insulation	TSI	M	15
Fire Damper	M	M	15
Flexible Fabric Joints (vibrating dampening cloth)	M	M	15
Duct Insulation	TSI	M	15
Ductwork Taping	M	M	15
Flue, Seam Taping	M	M	15
Cooling Tower, Fill	M	M	15
Cooling Tower, Baffles or Louvers	M	M	15
Valve packing	TSI	M	15
Plumbing, Piping Insulation	TSI	P	15
Plumbing, Pipe Gaskets	M	P	15
Plumbing, Equipment Insulation	TSI	P	15

51

EXHIBIT E-12 (cont.)

SUSPECT MATERIALS (continued)	MTRL TYPES	PLANS	SPECS
Electrical Ducts (cable chases)	M	E	16
Electrical Panel Partitions	M	E	16
Electrical Cloth	M	E	16
Insulation, Wiring	M	E	16
Stage Lighting	M	E	16
Incandescent Recessed Fixtures	M	E	16
Chalkboards	M	A	10

EXHIBIT E-13
TRADE NAMES OF ASBESTOS-CONTAINING PRODUCTS

The following list contains trade names which have been or are being used on products containing asbestos. This list is not all inclusive.
From: Sourcebook on Asbestos Diseases: Medical, Legal, and Engineering Aspects. Volume 2. George A. Peters and Barbara J. Peters. Garland Law Publishing, New York, 1986.

Aboglas	Asbestoroc
Accobest	Asbestos Ebony
Accobest AN-8012	Asbestos-Ebony
Acoa	Asbestos Firetard Jacket
Aertite	Asbestos Grapevine Finish Felt
AFD	Asbestos Liquid
Aircel	Asbestos Luminclad
Aircell	Asbestos Millboard
Akoustikos Felt	Asbestos Sponge
Aland	Asbestos Sponge Felt
Albaseal	Asbestos Roll Fire Felt
Aluman-Seal	Ascarite
Alum-I-Flex	Astrolan
Amberlite	Atlas
Amerbestos	Aubeston
American Colonial	BB
Anti-Sweat	BBA
Apac	Bellowseal
Apac Board	Best Felt
Applon C TFE	Bes-Tos
Applong T TFE	Bestolite
Armaturo Asbestos Tape	Bestphalt
Armor Spray	Beswick
Armor Temp	Black Top Asbestos
Armstrong LT Cork Coatings	Blastape
Asbaltic	Calidria Asbestos
Asbestall	Cal Temp
Asbestex	Caposite
Asbestibel	Carbac
Asbestile	Carey
Asbestite	Careybesto-Board
Asbestoboard	Careycel
Asbestocel	Caryclad
Asestocite	Carey Duct
Asbestogard	Careyflex
Asbestoluc	Careysote
Asbeston	Careystone
Asbestone 400	Careytemp
Asbestone Standard 400	Cedargrain

Cellamite
Cell-O-Tone
Cernesto
Cernesto Structural Insulating
Panels
Centripac
Century
Century Apac
Certain-Teed
Chemlon
Chempac
Chemstone
Chemtite
Chesterton Sixty Four
Chesterton 1,000
Chroma-Tex
Chroma-Tone
Chrom-Tex
Cleangard
Cogasa
Cohrlastic
Colonial
Colorator
Colorbestos
Color Ground
Cololith
Color-Tex
Contico
Coperclad
Coronet
Covergard
Crystal White
Cutno
C.W.
Deltabeston
Designer Solids
Dominique
Doublex
Double Sanded Asbestos
Dualay
Duplex
Dura-Color
Duraform
Dura Shake
Durocell
Du Shield
Ebonized Asbestos
Electrobestos

Enduro
Eternit
Eternit Stonewall
Excelon
Face Span
Featherweight
Felbestos
FI-ACS
Fiberock
Fiberock Asbestos Felt
Fiber Shake
Fiberspray Asbestos
Fibra Flow
FIbre Coating Asbestos
Fibre Kote
Fibrocel
FibroCell
Fibrofil
Fibro-Fill
Fibroid
Fibroid Stove Putty
Fil-Insul
Filpaco
Fire Chex
Fire-Chex
Fireclad
Fire Felt
Firegard
Fireguard Jacketing
Fire Halt
Firetard
Flamegard
Flamemaster
Flamesafe
FLexachrome
Flexboard
Flexgold
Flex-Slate
Flexstone
Flintite
Florobestos
F-M-C
F.O.P
Form Pack 2
Foster
Frost Proof
GAF
Gardian Line

Gardwell
Gardwell Products
Goetze Metallic Gaskets
Gold Bond
Grafel
Gralam
Grizzly
G.T. Ring
Gum-Bestos
Herco
Hi Seal
Hoodex-22
Hopaco
Horneblende
Hy Temp
Imperial
Imperial Excelon
Imperial Pipe Covering
Industrial
Industro-Tile
Insulation Seal 820
Insulcolor
Isobestos
Janobestos
Janos
Jewett
JM or Johns-Manville
Kaobestos
Kaylo
Kearsarge
K-Fac
Klingerit
K&M Aircell
Kormetal
K Therm
Lasco
Linalbestoos
LK
LO-CA
Lok-Tab
Marinite
Mastic
Maticove
McKim
Micabestos
Mightyplate
Mimco
Mikote

Modernaire
Monobestos
Monoblock
Montastite
Multi-Ply
Mundet
New Era
Niagarite
Nicolet
Non-Con-Dux
Noriscell
Novabestos
Nu Grain
Nu Side
Nu Way
Ohmstone
O.N.C.
One Cote Cement
Pabco
Pakmetal
Pal-Lite
Palmetto
Palmetto Cutno
Palmetto Super Shet
Pamco
Panelstone
Permaboard
Permatherm
Permatone
Piedra
Plastibest*
Plastic
PlastiClad
Plasticrylic
Pliaboard
Plia-F-Lex
Pluto
Portugese Asbestos
Powminco
Prasco High Temperature
Prenite
Prismatic
Profile
Pyrotex Felt
Q-Beston
Quinorgo
Quinterra
Ranch Style

Red Mastite
Rendezvous
Resistal
Ring-Tite
Ripple Tone
R-M or Raybestos-Manhatten
RM 7504
R/M 24 H120
R/M E-66
Roca Rock Slate
Romanaire
Rondelle
Rubber Coat
Salamander
Salon
Sal-Mo
Scandiva
Sea Ring Packing
Selko-Flo
Service Sheet Packing & Cut
Gaskets
Shasta Snow
Sheetflextos
ShingleSeal
Simco
Sindayano
Soundgard
Spintex
Spiroflex
Spirotallic
Splashgard
Spray-Cote
Spray Craft
Sprayed Limpet Asbestos
Sta Safe Long Life
Sterlbestos
Stik-On
Stone Chip
Stoneglow
Stonewall Board
Stratalite
Stri-Color
Strip-N-Lay
Summit
Superbestos
Super Cutno
Superheat
Super X

Super 66
Supradur
Sure-Stik
Tadpole
Target
Tempcheck
Terraflex
Terratex
Thermal Kote
Thermalon
Thermatite
Thermobestos
Thermo-Board
Thermofelt
Therm-O-Flake
Thermoflex
Thermomat
Thermo-Pac
Thermostone
Thermotape
Thermotex B
Thermo-Wrap
Thrift T
Thru/Chip
Tile-Tex
Tilostone TK 33
Transhield
Transite
Transite-Korduct
Transitop
Tru Flame
Tropag
U.F.P.
Unibestos
Unibestos 750
Unibestos 1200
Uni Syn
Uni Syn Style o. 239
V Dent Ventsulation
Victopac
Vitribestos
Vitrobestos
Vulca-Dek
Weldgard
White Top Asbestos Jacket
Whitaker
Wirepack

EXHIBIT E-14
CONSTRUCTION SPECIFICATIONS INSTITUTE (CSI) MASTERFORMAT

Division	0	conditions of the contract
Division	1	general requirements
Division	2	site work
Division	3	concrete
Division	4	masonry
Division	5	metals
Division	6	wood and plastics
Division	7	thermal and moisture protection
Division	8	doors and windows
Division	9	finishes
Division	10	specialties
Division	11	equipment
Division	12	furnishings
Division	13	special construction
Division	14	conveying systems
Division	15	mechanical
Division	16	electrical

The Occupational Safety and Health Administration (OSHA) Worker Exposure
Rules for Asbestos (1994) include requirements for notification, warning signs
and labels, and education programs on the part of any employer whose
employees are exposed to asbestos fiber levels above the exposure standard.
The permissible exposure limit (PEL) is currently 0.1 fibers per cubic centimeter
(f/cc) of air, averaged over an 8-hour day. OSHA has established an excursion
limit (EL) as well. If employees are exposed to a time-weighted average of 0.1
f/cc over an 8-hour period (the PEL) employers must begin compliance activities
such as notification, air monitoring, and employee training. The excursion limit is
1.0 f/cc averaged over a 30 minute time period, and is generally targeted for
those individuals who may be exposed to high airborne asbestos fiber
concentrations for short time periods. The Regulatory Review section of the
course notebook covers the activities which trigger the requirements of the
OSHA regulations in greater detail.

The Environmental Protection Agency (EPA) recommends that building owners
inform building occupants of the presence an location of asbestos-containing
materials (ACM) and the need to avoid disturbing them even if fiber levels are
below he OSHA exposure limits. Accidental disturbance of the ACM could easily
raise airborne fiber levels to or above the OSHA exposure levels mentioned
above.

The local education agency (LEA)/building owner has three major concerns.
First, building occupants should be informed of any potential hazard in the
building. Second, building occupants who are informed and instructed about
ACM are less likely to disturb the material and cause fibers to be released. Third,
early and full disclosure may reduce legal liabilities and the likelihood of future
litigation.

The best approach to handling public, employee, and building occupant relations
when dealing with asbestos involved three principles:
- Bring it up early
- Tell the truth
- Communicate with all affected parties

RELEVANCE TO BUILDING INSPECTORS AND MANAGEMENT PLANNERS

Both the Building Inspector and Management Planner have a stake in assisting
the LEA or building owner in developing a public relations program. The
inspector is likely to have the first contact with building occupants and workers
and should be prepared to explain his/her activities in an accurate and
acceptable (to the building owner) manner. The building owner may also want to
initiate a full disclosure program at the time of the inspection rather than waiting
for the results of the inspector's survey. If ACM is found, the Management

Planner should work with the LEA to develop a more complete public relations program.

Disclosure can begin before the inspection is done or the results are known and can include the following as a typical disclosure/information outline:
1. Inspection activity/access
2. Purpose of inspection-to determine whether asbestos is present
3. Information available-upon receipt of lab results
4. Possible response actions
5. Concern for maintaining safe environment
6. Person/office to contact for additional information

BUILDING INSPECTOR

At a minimum, the building inspector and those assisting him/her must reach an understanding with the LEA or building owner on how questions from building employees and occupants are to be handled. Exhibit F-1 is a suggested informational handout which can be tailored for circulation prior to or at the time of an inspection. It is necessary to know how your client wants you to deal with requests for further clarification from persons observing your activities. You may be authorized to elaborate on the inspection, or you may be told to refer all persons making inquiries to the building owner or his representative. In no case should the inspector provide or present information which is not true.

MANAGEMENT PLANNER

The Management Planner is likely to be called upon to assume a prominent role in planning the LEA's public relations program. The planner will provide expertise, credibility, and assurances to effectively deal with the questions and concerns of building workers and occupants.

COMMUNICATION

Building occupants, whether employees of the building owner or not, can be informed of potential or confirmed building hazards in at least three ways:
1. By distributing notices
2. Posting signs
3. Holding awareness or informational meetings

SECTION F: PUBLIC /EMPLOYEE/BUILDING OCCUPANT
RELATIONS\REQUIREMENTS AND RECOMMENDATIONS

The method(s) chosen may depend upon the type and location of the ACM and on the number of people affected. Some states have "right-to-know" laws. In such states it may be required that all occupants as well as visitors to buildings with ACM be informed that asbestos is present.

Exhibits F-2 and F-3 are examples of communication/informational materials.

The U.S. EPA has issued notification requirements associated with its targeting and implementation of asbestos regulations for schools, and these requirements may make useful guidelines for notification in non-school settings as well. Under the 1982 Friable Asbestos-Containing Materials in Schools: Identification and Notification Rule, administrators of primary and secondary schools were required by EPA to inform employees and parent-teacher groups about the presence of any friable asbestos in their schools. In addition, administrators were required to distribute specific instructions on handling ACM to custodial and maintenance workers.

The Asbestos Hazard Emergency Response Act (AHERA) adopted many of the 1982 rule's requirements and expanded upon them. A building owner or LEA can use the information generated by the building inspector's activities in a comprehensive public relations program which will provide accurate and reliable information to building occupants. An overview of an LEA's notification responsibilities is presented in the Management Planner notebook under the section "Developing and Implementing an Operations and Maintenance Program."

OSHA requires that building or facility owners notify their own employees, tenants, and the employees of other contractors on multi-employer worksites prior to beginning certain activities involving the removal or disturbance of asbestos. This includes identifying the presence, location, and quantity of ACM or presumed ACM (PACM).

SIGNS AND NOTICES

Under AHERA, signs containing the words:

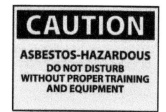

CAUTION
ASBESTOS—HAZARDOUS
DO NOT DISTURB WITHOUT PROPER
TRAINING AND EQUIPMENT

Are required to be placed immediately adjacent to any friable and non-friable ACM as well as suspected ACM located in routine maintenance areas. All signs must be prominently displayed in clearly visible locations. They must remain posted on all ACBM until it is removed. Warning signs will serve to alert and remind building occupants not to disturb ACM. Frequently, areas such as boiler rooms are posted with signs which restrict access to everyone except service personnel who need to work there.

The specific wording of notices and signs is important. From a legal perspective, the presentation may affect the building owner's liability if building occupants are exposed to asbestos. To be effective communication devices, warning signs or notices should:

- Be tailored to the people and the environment in which they are used
- Communicate in a language understood by the audience
- Be practical; they cannot prohibit activities necessary for individuals to perform their assigned jobs
- Attract attention
- Be durable and be replaced as necessary

The OSHA standards require the establishment of <u>regulated areas</u> where airborne concentrations of asbestos exceed or are expected to exceed the PEL or EL, or where certain activities take place. Warning signs must be displayed at each regulated area and at all approaches to regulated areas. The information contained on these warning signs is prescribed by OSHA and must state:

DANGER
ASBESTOS
CANCER AND LUNG DISEASE HAZARD
AUTHORIZED PERSONNEL ONLY

EDUCATION

The OSHA standards state that the employer/building owner <u>must</u> develop and present a training program for all employees who will remove, disturb, or contact ACM or PACM. This program must be provided to all current employees, to all new staff prior to or at the time of initial employment, and the training must be repeated on a yearly basis thereafter. The detail of the training will vary according to the degree of activity and disturbance of the asbestos-containing material. (See the Regulatory Review section for more detail on OSHA training requirements.)

Any educational effort undertaken by a building owner should include the following information:

- Asbestos is present in the building
- They type and location of the asbestos
- The potential health effects of asbestos exposure
- Plans to deal with the problem

- Instructions to avoid disturbing the ACM (e.g. do not hang plants, do not move ceiling tiles, etc.)
- Procedures to report any disturbance or damage to ACM
- Additional sources of information
- A record of all attendees and the dates of training.

Information/education sessions reinforce and clarify written notices. In addition they provide an opportunity to answer questions, transmit accurate information, provide assurances that responsible, appropriate action is being take and to defuse unwarranted concerns.

TIMING

Credibility is what the employer, building owner, or school administrator is seeking in a public relations effort. Information flow should begin before the inspection process to establish credibility and should be reinforced by timely updates as further information becomes available for distribution. Presenting the logic and rationale for the actions being taken may encourage cooperation.

It is in the best interests of the building owner to schedule any announcements or distribute written notices to building occupants simultaneously. Establish a fixed time and place to meet with all concerned parties. Allow sufficient time to respond to questions and address concerns. Identify person(s) to contact regarding questions that arise in the future.

An outline of general design considerations for a sound public relations effort is presented in Exhibit F-4.

**EXHIBIT F-1
SAMPLE INSPECTOR HANDOUT**

SURVEY OF BUILDING MATERIALS

_____(The School Board/Building Owner) is undertaking a survey of its/his/her buildings to determine if any of the building materials contain asbestos. Asbestos has been widely used in building construction. The (Board/Owner) believes that a complete survey of all facilities is the most prudent approach to assuring protection to all personnel and building occupants.

Within the next (few months) specially trained and accredited inspectors will be visiting this building to inspect for suspect materials. To determine whether suspect materials contain asbestos, samples must be collected and submitted for laboratory analysis. Please cooperate in every way with them. In the event that asbestos is discovered, action will be taken to maintain safe conditions.

You may see the inspector wearing a respirator. This is precautionary measure designed to provide the inspector with protection from any exposure that he or she may accumulated during hundreds of inspection and sampling operations.

If you have any questions about the survey, please _____

EXHIBIT F-2
SAMPLE INFORMATIONAL LETTER TO EMPLOYEES

Acme Insurance Company
1 Auto Place
Business, XX 01111

Ms. Merry M. Played
222 Workhorse Road
Business, XX 01111

Dear Ms. Ployee: 15 October 2012

An important matter has been brought to my attention that I feel requires
personal communication to all of our employees. As you may know, plans have
been underway for several months for a major renovation of the space on the
first floor into a new and expanded computer facility. At the initial stages of the
renovation, some suspect material was found behind the existing walls. Samples
were obtained and analyzed by an outside laboratory and this material was
shown to contain asbestos.

After extensive discussion with the Board of Directors, as well as reputable
experts in the field of asbestos, the decision was reached to inspect the entire
facility for the presence of asbestos.

I have instructed each department to appoint a representative to attend the first
of many meetings of an Asbestos Task Force. This meeting will be held in
conference room 110 at 4 p.m. on Tuesday, October 20, 2002. This Task Force
will receive briefings from departments already involved with the upcoming
survey (i.e., Building Services, Environmental Services, Security). I will present
to deliver my own thoughts as well as to represent the Board of Directors. We will
also have Dr. L. E. Mentary, Chief of Pulmonary Service for General Hospital; Mr.
I.M. Brief, Esq., Senior Partner of Short, Sweet, and Brief, P.C. our corporate
attorneys; and Ms. Ellie Ectron, an experienced asbestos and air quality analyst.
These individuals will provide a knowledgeable and experienced panel to answer
any questions you might have.

One of the most important elements of sampling material suspected of containing
asbestos is the use of protective equipment. For a survey, the inspector will be
wearing a respirator. This is the required protection for those people who actually
handle the materials in order to remove a small sample. Please do not be
alarmed when you see these individuals using personal protective equipment
and clothing. These individuals are trained to use extreme caution when taking
samples to prevent release of any fibers. When an inspector is in your area,
allow him/her free access to any area necessary. The results of laboratory tests

on these samples will be communicated through your department's task force representative.

I appreciate this opportunity to discuss this very important matter with each of our employees. If you have any questions or concerns, please telephone me personally. My office extension is x-1111, or send correspondence through inter-office mail addressed to my attention. Thank you.

Yours truly,

Charles M. Gee
Vice President

EXHIBIT F-3 PRESS RELEASE (Example)

ANSWANEEE COUNTY ADMINISTRATOR,
ANYTOWN, USA-

MARCH 26, 2012

IMMEDIATE RELEASE

The chairman of the Answanee county Council announced today that asbestos-containing insulation materials have been found in the County Administration Building. The materials are used to insulate hot water piping and forced air ductwork. All of the asbestos is now enclosed by impregnated wrappings designed to prevent fiber release.

"We have had credentialed industrial hygienists monitor air quality in the building for several days," said Council Chairman Verne T. Hicks, "and the levels of asbestos fibers are considerably lower than Federal government (OSHA) standards. We believe that there is simply no cause for concern about the health of employees, tenants, or the general public, because the levels are not substantially different from those found outside the building in similar sampling."

According to Hicks, the Occupational Safety and Health Administration requires that the levels of asbestos fibers in the workplace not exceed a concentration of 0.2 fibers per cubic centimeter of air (8-hour time-weighted average). The highest level measured in the County Administration Building was 0.01 fibers per cubic centimeter. The analysis of the air sample was not specific for asbestos fibers and may include other fiber types. "And even that figure is speculative," added Hicks, "because of practical limits of measurement employed by hygienists, we feel there should be no worry by anyone using our building."

Exposure to asbestos fibers has been linked to a variety of diseases, including cancer. Asbestos was heavily used in the construction and shipbuilding industries from World War II through the early 1970s because of its excellent properties related to thermal insulation. In recent years, Federal programs have called for asbestos inspections in the nation's schools; school age children are the focus of this program intended to reduce the exposure level for their generation.

County Administrator Charles A. Lessing announced the appointment of the Assistant Public Services Director, John Smallwood, to the interim position of "Asbestos Coordinator." According to Lessing, Smallwood's duties include acting as the central point of all information about the presence of asbestos and directing any plans regarding the material.

"Currently, building maintenance personnel are the only individuals likely to come into contact with the asbestos," said Smallwood. He noted that some of the pipes and ducts wrapped with the material are visible in general office areas and

66

corridors, but a person would have to get up on a chair and willfully damage the wrapping to cause any potential contamination. Smallwood has established a special "Operations and Maintenance Plan" for the protection of the maintenance workers.

Council Chairman Hicks said that some asbestos-containing material would be removed and replaced with other insulation as funding becomes available and time permits. Several feet of deteriorated pipe insulation in the boiler room will be replaced next month as soon as bids are received on a contract now being developed.

Briefings have been held for occupants of the building, including county employees and tenant personnel. Smallwood said "An information brochure has been written for the general public using the building, and this brochure is available at the main lobby and all normal places of contact with county employees." A special letter is being mailed to each service or utility contractor who has occasion to work in the building, as the telephone company.

In addition to the industrial hygiene firm which conducted air monitoring and analyzed bulk samples of the suspect materials, the county has retained the firm of Squantum Engineers to prepare specifications for removal of asbestos. Council Chairman Hicks also said the county may look into possible recovery of costs. "We are talking with an attorney who is experienced in asbestos litigation, and we expect some advice along these lines within a month."

All questions concerning the asbestos-containing material in the county Administration Building should be referred to the Asbestos Coordinator, John Smallwood.

EXHIBIT F-4 PUBLIC RELATIONS

I. Purpose
   a. Answer critics
   b. Provide information
   c. Separate facts from fiction
   d. Allow decisions
   e. Encourage cooperation
   f. Confirm integrity
   g. Encourage participation
   h. Prescribe procedures
   i. Identify parameters
   j. Show commitment
   k. Reduce anxiety

II. Targets
   a. Internal
      i. Employees
      ii. Occupants
   b. External
      i. Press
      ii. Parents
      iii. Neighbors
      iv. Vendors
      v. Visitors

III. Media
   a. Written
      i. Letter
      ii. Guidance document
      iii. Policy
   b. Posted
      i. Notice
      ii. Warning
   c. Presented
      i. Public gathering
   d. Recorded
      i. Video
      ii. Photographic

IV. Format
   a. Language
   b. Tone
   c. Accuracy
   d. Simplicity
   e. Context
   f. Sufficiency
   g. Truth

V. Content
   a. Past

        i. Context
        ii. Progress
   b. Present
        i. Dilemma
        ii. Options
        iii. Plan
   c. Future
        i. Intentions

VI.   Must be
   a. Aimed
        i. Personalities
           1. Facts→ possibilities
           2. Warmth→ impersonal
        ii. Filters
           1. Education
           2. Mood
           3. Politics
           4. Risk
   b. Received
   c. Understood
   d. Believed
   e. Appreciated

INTRODUCTION

The process of inspecting a facility for the presence of asbestos-containing materials is a complex task involving a great deal of pre-planning and cooperation among affected parties. This section is intended to prepare an Inspector for the job ahead by providing an overview of the following items:

- Members of the inspection team
- Types of buildings and inspections
- Informing non-participants
- Pre-inspection meetings
- Review of previous inspections
- Review of building records
- Organizing the inspection
- Criteria for exclusion under AHERA for previously performed inspections

THE INSPECTION TEAM

The inspection team should consist of the building owner's representative (the "asbestos program manager" as described in EPA's green Book or the "designated person" in the language of AHERA), the original building architect (if available), the facilities manager or maintenance director, and the consultant's staff if an outside consultant is employed. The designated person is the Inspector's key contact. This person will have some training in asbestos management (the AHERA rule specifies general areas but not the type and duration of training), and will be responsible for making arrangements, assuring access to records, staff, and buildings, and providing necessary support to conduct the investigation. He or she will also direct the investigation if it is conducted solely with in-house staff. Others who may serve as advisors to the team include the EPA Regional Asbestos Coordinator and the building owner's attorney. The building owner or school administrator should assure the cooperation of all relevant staff members.

TYPES OF BUILDINGS AND INSPECTORS

The building inspector may be faced with a great variety of buildings and several levels of inspection. Schools (typically one or several stories), small office buildings, high rises, and a large volume structures (e.g., warehouses) all present different inspection challenges. Inspections can range from a quick verification of a single type of suspected ACM in preparation for facility renovation, to a complete investigation leading to a comprehensive management plan. The emphasis here is on schools and office buildings , and on complete investigations.

With respect to AHERA, all public and private primary and secondary schools must be inspected. This includes all structures used for teaching and related activities, and all mechanical and support facilities. ASHARA, although not requiring inspections of public and commercial buildings, does require the use of accredited inspectors for all inspections conducted within those facilities. Good practice will usually dictate that ASHARA inspections be conducted similarly to AHERA inspections. In addition to AHERA and ASHARA, the U.S. EPA's National Emission Standards for Hazardous Air Pollutants (NESHAP) regulations require that a facility be inspected for the presence of ACM prior to demolition or renovation which may disturb asbestos. (See Section L, "Regulatory Review" for more detail on these regulations.)

INFORMING NON-PARTICIPANTS

Some school administrators or building owners may wish to inform employees, building occupants, parents, and even the public about the pending inspection. Others will want to wait until the results of the inspection are known before publicizing the inspection. See Section F on public relations for more information on procedures used to notify others of ACM detection and control activities.

GETTING STARTED

Initial meetings with building owners and/or their representatives should focus on the history of concerns about asbestos in the building, including any previous investigations for ACM. All records, reports, plans, and narrative accounts relevant to asbestos should be identified in this initial meeting. In addition, architects, contractors, maintenance personnel, and others knowledgeable about (possible) ACM in the building should be identified. Arrangements should then be made to assemble and review relevant documents, conduct interviews, if necessary, and to conduct the building inspection. Where possible, the inspection should be planned for off-hour times, that is, times when the building is largely unoccupied. However, it is important for inspectors to gain complete understanding of typical or anticipated activities in the building while it is fully occupied.

REVIEWING PREVIOUS INVESTIGATIONS

Many school districts will have completed an asbestos investigation in compliance with the 1982 EPA "Schools Rule." (Investigations were to have been completed by June 1983.) Reviewing the results of any previous investigation (reports of building inspections and bulk sample analyses) is a logical starting point for this investigation. Where ACM has been positively identified, the results can be accepted at face value. Where the previous findings were negative (no friable materials were discovered or friable materials were found not to contain asbestos), or where non-friable materials were not investigated, the investigation will likely need to be repeated. The failure to employ a random sampling scheme for friable surfacing materials and for most thermal system insulation and the failure to inspect for non-friable materials likely to contain asbestos are the two major deficiencies in most prior investigations. Where the previous investigation is in conformance with all the AHERA requirements, the Building inspector will simply verify this in writing.

Even where the investigation must be repeated, results of the previous study should make this one more efficient. The sources of information used by the previous inspector should be identified in his/her report; these can be reviewed quickly to verify the accuracy of the data, and attention can then turn to identifying sources of suspect material missed or ignored.

Recall that AHERA does not require an investigation for all ACM. Instead, only asbestos-containing building material (ACBM) needs to be identified and documented. ACBM excludes most exterior products and most fabric materials. However, a comprehensive investigation will include all suspect materials wherever they are located.

INSPECTING BUILDING RECORDS

Where available, plans (or "working drawings") and record documents should be reviewed to obtain an initial orientation to the layout and structural/electrical/mechanical elements of the building. Change orders and specifications should be reviewed for any reference to asbestos materials generically or by manufacturer or brand name. (See Section E "Understanding Building Systems" for a discussion of building documents and a list of asbestos products by brand name.) Mention of miscellaneous (largely non-friable) asbestos building products such as asbestos-cement wallboard or pipe is especially significant since identifying non-friable ACM or suspect non-friable materials in the field is often difficult. Discussions with persons involved with the original construction or with subsequent renovations will sometimes reveal information on ACM not contained in building records. Such persons should be asked if anyone ever mentioned that building materials contain or might contain asbestos, or if they recall mention of any asbestos product manufacturers or their products (read or show persons the list of brand name products in Section E) during or after construction. Other records and documents to review include a site plan or physical description of the type, size, and number of buildings which make up the facility, construction field reports if available, photographic records, and any equipment or information sources mentioned above are a starting point only. An Inspector will still need to physically and visually inspect the building and collect samples and have them analyzed to definitively identify the presence of asbestos.

72

Where previously identified ACM has been partially or completed abated (removed, enclosed, or encapsulated), this should be verified by reviewing abatement records and inspecting the location or previous location of the ACM during the building inspection. Abatement records should indicate that the abatement work passed a visual inspection and, preferably, an air test. The field inspection should focus on the integrity of the abatement, that is, the completeness of the removal, the integrity of the <u>enclosure</u>, or the coverage of the <u>encapsulant</u>. The presence of all remaining ACM should be documented in the new report.

ORGANIZING THE BUILDING INSPECTION

The inspection should be organized by type of ACM and by floor and area within the building. An initial building walk-through will provide a general orientation. Then, starting from the bottom floor and working toward the top, each area within each floor should be systematically inspected for (1) surfacing material, (2) thermal system insulation (TSO), and (3) miscellaneous products. Knowledge of the building's layout, structural features, and mechanical systems (gained from building documents and the initial walk-through) should be used to assure a thorough inspection.

The availability of a maintenance employee or other individual intimately familiar with building and mechanical system layout will greatly enhance the Inspector's ability to perform a thorough inspection. This individual can also assist in providing access to areas and materials to be inspected. Some experienced inspectors may be choose to combine the inspection for miscellaneous products with the inspection for one of the other two categories of suspect materials. But since the procedures for identifying sampling areas differ for surfacing material and thermal insulation, it is best to conduct separate inspections for these materials. Inspection includes:
- Identification of <u>homogeneous sampling areas</u> and <u>functional spaces</u>
- Collection of bulk samples
- <u>Physical assessment</u> and classification of the material

As an alternative to sampling and analysis, the suspect material can be assumed to contain asbestos.

Exhibit G-1 is a list of general types of areas to be inspected in various types of buildings. This can serve as a general check list to help insure that the entire building has been inspected. This list also serves to identify types of functional spaces which need to be assessed. Functional spaces are areas defined by walls or physical barriers and which contain a population of service workers, residents, other building occupants, or visitors. (Functional spaces and the physical assessment process are discussed in Section H, "Inspecting for Friable

73

and Nonfriable Asbestos-Containing Material and Assessing the Condition of Friable ACM.")

Exhibit G-2 is a summary list of documents that can be used to both plan the inspection and record data. A plot plan provides a view of the entire building and the site. Floor plans can be used to develop a step-by-step plan for the field work. The location of ACM as specified in building plans or other sources of information can be plotted on the floor plans. Using the same information, sampling areas can be preliminarily delineated on the floor plans as well. IN addition to functional spaces, homogeneous sampling areas must be delineated by the building inspector for purposes of selecting area sample locations. Section I, "Bulk Sampling and Documentation," contains detailed instructions on delineating homogeneous sampling areas. Final delineation of homogeneous sampling areas must await actual inspection of the suspect materials in the building. If floor plans drawn approximately to scale are not available, rough scale drawings for each floor should be made on graph paper.

FINALIZING THE INSPECTION PLAN

Protocols for conducting the inspection should be finalized and agreed upon at this point. This includes all procedures to be used in identifying friable and non-friable materials likely to contain asbestos, and all data collection forms. Standardization of these procedures is critical. (See Sections H and I for more information.)

Next, arrangements should be made to schedule the actual inspection. Consider the availability of all affected parties, including the inspection team and other pertinent individuals, especially those who will provide access to the areas to be inspected.

Laboratories for analyzing bulk samples should also be selected at this time. Laboratories which participate in the National Institute of Standards and Technology (NIST) National Voluntary Laboratory Accreditation Program (NVLAP) are required to be used under AHERA. (See Section I for more information on selecting laboratories.)

REQUIREMENTS AND EXCLUSIONS UNDER AHERA

The AHERA Rule requires that all suspect materials be identified, located, and documented, and that friable suspect surfacing and miscellaneous materials and TSI be assessed and classified. Under certain circumstances, the local education agency (LEA) may not be required to inspect their buildings. The criteria for exclusion are:

1.	An accredited Inspector has determined that friable asbestos-containing building material (ACBM) was identified during and inspection conducted prior to October 17, 1987. However, the accredited Inspector still must assess the friable ACBM.

74

2. An accredited Inspector has determined that non-friable ACBM was identified during an inspection conducted prior to October 17, 1987. However, the accredited Inspector shall identify whether material that was non-friable has become friable since the previous inspection and shall assess the newly friable ACBM.

3. An accredited inspector has determined (based on sampling and inspection records) that no ACBM is present and the records show that the area was sampled, before October 17, 1987, in substantial compliance with the regulation, (i.e., a sufficient number of samples taken in a random manner).

4. The appropriate state agency (granted a waiver from §763.85 (a)) has determined that no ACBM is present and the records show that the area was sampled, before October 17, 1987, in substantial compliance with the regulations.

5. The accredited Inspector has determined (based on inspection and sampling records conducted before October 17, 1987) that suspected ACBM will be assumed to be ACM. However, the inspector shall identify whether material assumed to be non-friable ACBM has become friable, and assess that newly friable material

6. The accredited inspector has determined that no ACBM is present where asbestos removal operations have been conducted before October 17, 1987.

7. An architect or project engineer responsible for construction of a new school building built after October 12, 1988, or an accredited Inspector, signs a statement that no ACBM was specified as a building material, and to the best of his/her knowledge, no ACBM was used as a building material

It is important to note that exclusions to the AHERA inspection requirements listed above apply only to schools that were inspected and sampled before October 17, 1987, unless otherwise indicated. Also, if ACBM is subsequently found to be present, the LEA will have 180 days to comply with the AHERA inspection requirements.

EXHIBIT G-1
GENERAL CATEGORIES OF BUILDING AREAS TO BE INSPECTED

I.   Mechanical Areas
        Basement/sublevel service areas
                Boiler/Chiller Rooms
                Generator Rooms
                Elevator equipment rooms
                Telephone/electrical rooms
                Mechanical feed distribution rooms
                Fan rooms
                Basements
                Furnace rooms
                Tunnels and crawl spaces
        Mechanical Floors Including Penthouse (which may contain the above rooms as well)
                Attics
                Air/Duct shafts
                Pipe chases
                Air plenums
                Elevator shafts and machine rooms
II.   Common Areas
        Entrance and exit areas
        Lobbies
        Hallways
        Stairwells
        Meeting rooms (e.g., auditoriums, conference rooms, lounges)
        Garages
III.   Living/Working Areas
        Offices
        Hotel rooms
        Rooms in apartments or single family houses
        Hospital rooms
IV.   Special Use Rooms
        Kitchens
        Dining rooms
        Laundries
        Vaults
        Athletic facilities (e.g., pools, gyms, locker rooms)

EXHIBIT G-2
**USEFUL DOCUMENTS FOR ORGANIZING THE INSPECTION AND
RECORDING INFORMATION**

Document	Use
Site Plan	Provides overall perspective on the building and site -property lines -location of building -grading/drainage, etc.
Plans-specifications/ addenda-change orders/ record documents- renovation drawings- other building documents	Provide information on (1) building systems finishes, and construction, and (2) specifications of ACM and substitute materials.
Previous Inspection Reports	Should provide a starting point. Identified ACM should be verified. Inadequate parts Of the inspection should be repeated.
Abatement Records	Indicate disposition of previously identified ACM. All records should be verified in the field.
Floor Plans	Can be used to (1) locate and document suspect material which is not sampled (misc. products), (2) delineate homogeneous sampling areas, (3) identify locations of bulk samples, and (4) record functional spaces.

77

INTRODUCTION

The inspection process focuses on identifying (1) <u>surfacing materials</u>, (2) <u>thermal system insulation</u> (TSI) and (3) <u>miscellaneous materials</u>, all of which are likely to contain asbestos. Once these are located, <u>homogeneous sampling areas</u> (areas which are uniform by color, texture, construction/application date, and general appearance) are delineated and the suspect materials are sampled and analyzed for asbestos (see Section I, "Bulk Sampling and Documentation"). If suspect materials are not sampled, they should be assumed to contain asbestos. <u>Functional spaces</u> are then identified for purposes of assessing all friable suspect material and thermal system insulation. Review the types and specific examples of ACM described in Section A "Background Information on Asbestos," and Section E "Understanding Building Systems".

The inspection and assessment process can be summarized as follows:

1. Assemble equipment and supplies
2. Obtain copies of the floor plans for the building or draw plans approximately to scale.
3. Locate any materials specified as asbestos-containing in the construction documents.
4. Walk through the building starting at the lowest floor and proceed to the highest floor. (The assistance of someone familiar with the building is usually very helpful.)
5. Enter every room and utility space, including crawl spaces, to look for suspect materials. Included: mechanical rooms (boiler/chiller, generator, elevator equipment, telephone/electrical rooms, air-handling and fan rooms, cable and equipment vaults), loading docks, attached garages, attics, air shafts and pipe chases, and special use areas (laundries, kitchens and dining areas, conference rooms, pools, gyms, locker rooms, and auditoriums). Also, be sure to inspect above suspended ceilings wherever observed, all the way to the ceiling deck or roof deck.
6. Test (touch) all surfaces (walls, ceilings, structural members) for friability.
7. Record the location and a description of all suspect materials assumed to be ACBM.
8. For all suspect materials to be sampled, identify and draw homogeneous sampling areas (see Section I for specific instructions).
9. For all friable suspect materials and thermal system insulation, identify (with an I.D. code) and locate appropriate functional spaces on the floor plans.
10. Assess friable suspect material and thermal system insulation and record assessment.

AHERA REQUIREMENTS

78

Inspection and physical assessment requirements for primary and secondary schools are summarized in a flow diagram in Exhibit H-1 and in tabular form in Exhibit H-2. Listed are the types of suspect materials that should be inspected and sampled (or assumed to be ACM), and the subset that should be assessed. The type and number of samples to be collected as specified in the AHERA Rule are also indicated. Although AHERA only requires that schools be inspected, the AHERA inspection protocol can be adapted and used for other situations.

Asbestos Inspections

The specific requirements of AHERA are:
- Before October 12, 1988, Local Education Agencies (LEAs) must have inspected each building leased, owned, or used as a school to identify friable and nonfriable ACBM.
- Accredited inspectors must have been used for the inspection (Note: The Asbestos School Hazard Abatement Reauthorization Act (ASHARA) requires that if an asbestos inspection is conducted in a public or commercial building, including industrial facilities, an accredited Building Inspector must be used.)
- Reinspections using accredited building inspectors are required to be conducted at least once every three years following the implementation of the school's <u>management plan</u>.
- Inspection includes observing and touching all suspect materials, identifying the type of material, either sampling suspect materials or assuming they contain asbestos, and documenting the location of the material.
- All areas where friable suspect or assumed materials are located and areas where previously identified ACBM is located must be assessed.
- Friable materials and all thermal system insulation in each area assessed shall be placed in one of the following categories:
  1. Damaged or significantly damaged thermal system insulation
  2. Damaged friable surfacing ACM
  3. Significantly damaged friable surfacing ACM
  4. Damaged or significantly damaged friable miscellaneous ACM.
  5. ACBM with potential for damage
  6. ACBM with potential for significant damage
  7. Any remaining friable ACBM or friable suspected ACBM.
- ACBM in each of the damage categories should be described with respect to the type and extent of damage, the potential for disturbance, and the cause of damage.
- Schools to not have to be inspected if:
  o An accredited inspector has determined that a previous inspector identified all ACBM or indicated no ACBM present

(Note, however that any friable known or assumed ACBM must still be assessed.)

o   For schools built after 10/12/88, an architect or project engineer responsible for the construction of the building signs a statement that no ACBM was specified, or an accredited inspector certifies that no ACBM was used

o   Inspection and abatement records indicate all ACBM has been removed (See page G-4 for additional information on exceptions to inspection requirements.)

INSPECTION PROCEDURES

Recall the design for inspecting a building discussed in Section G ("Pre-Inspection Planning and Review of Previous Inspection Records")—an initial building walk-through followed by a floor-by-floor, area-by-area inspection, starting at the lowest floor. This section focuses on the inspection procedures to be used in each area of the building.

GENERAL

Assemble the materials needed to conduct the inspection:
- Flashlights, ladders, tape measure
- Respirators and protective clothing (see Section J, "Personal Protective Equipment")
- Sampling kit (see Section I)
- Recording and assessment forms, clipboard, pencil
- Other accessories

The building owner should provide an escort to open doors and assure access to all building spaces. This person is typically on the maintenance or engineering staff, and could provide a wealth of information about the building. Don't, however, be misled by statements that no ACM was used in the building, or that all ACM was completely removed. The building inspector is responsible for verifying these statements.

SURFACING MATERIALS

The friability of material on a building surface (walls, ceilings, wide flange beams, or other structural members) can only be determined by touch. If a powder can be generated by rubbing your hand across it, the material is friable. However, material that is otherwise friable may be made nonfriable (by the definition) by painting it, for example. Examine all painted or encapsulated surfacing materials carefully. Test

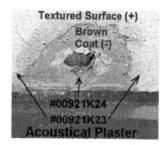

Textured Surface (+)
Brown Coat (-)
#00921K24
#00921K23
Acoustical Plaster

the surface for friability where is may be damaged or where the paint or encapsulant may be thinly applied or deteriorated. If the material proves to be friable during any of these tests, consider the entire surface friable. All friable material must be assessed as per AHERA. Note: respiratory protection may be necessary while testing for friability.

All friable and most nonfriable surfacing materials are suspect, which includes hard plaster (sand or smooth finish) as well as acoustical plaster. Textured paints may also be suspect. Substrates to which surfacing materials are applied, such as cinder blocks, steel, and wood are not suspect.

THERMAL SYSTEM INSULATION

All thermal system insulation should be considered suspect unless it can be unambiguously identified as non-asbestos. For example, fibrous glass pipe lagging has a characteristic pink or yellow color and a characteristic softness when squeezed. (Fiberglass will also resume its shape after being squeezed, as opposed to corrugated asbestos paper-air cell insulation.) Rubber

and Styrofoam can also be distinguished from other types of insulation by their color and texture. All block insulation on boiler and breeching, all cements and pipe-fitting muds, and all gasket materials should be considered suspect. Take care to inspect materials that maybe e covered up by a surface wrap of asbestos-free material. For example, fibrous glass insulation may have been installed over ACM on a pipe.

MISCELLANEOUS MATERIALS

The primary materials of concern in this category are floor and ceiling tiles. Include all lay-in ceiling tile and vinyl and asphalt floor tiles as suspect ACM. They must either be sampled and analyzed or assumed to contain asbestos. Asbestos-cement wallboard should also be inventoried, if present, as well as dry wall which is a suspect material. Fabric materials such as stage curtains and laboratory

gloves are not considered asbestos-containing building materials (ACBM) by the AHERA Rule, but should be included in a comprehensive building survey. Likewise, exterior materials such as roofing felt and siding need not be identified under AHERA or ASHARA, but should be recorded in a comprehensive survey. See Exhibit E-6 for a comprehensive list of suspect ACM.

81

RECORDING INFORMATION

For all suspect materials delineate homogeneous sampling areas on floor plans or approximately to-scale drawings (see Section I). These materials are either sampled and analyzed for asbestos or assumed to contain asbestos. For all suspect materials assumed to contain asbestos, record their location on floor plans or scale drawings. In addition, information on the type, location, and general condition of the assumed ACBM should be recorded on the "Assumed ACBM Location Form" (Exhibit H-3).

CONDUCTING THE PHYSICAL ASSESSMENT OF SUSPECT MATERIALS

AHERA specifies that the building inspector is to conduct a <u>physical assessment</u> of all friable suspect materials and all thermal system insulation. (If bulk sampling has been completed, only friable known and assumed ACBM and known and assumed thermal system insulation need to be assessed.) The physical assessment consists of assessing (1) the condition of the suspect material and (2) the potential for future disturbance. Following the assessment, all assessed ACBM is placed in one of the seven categories of condition and potential for disturbance. AHERA also requires that the results of the physical assessment be interpreted in terms of the hazard created by the ACBM. This is called a <u>hazard assessment</u> and is conducted by the Management Planner.

AIR MONITORING

The traditional approach to assessing hazards from airborne contaminants is to measure the concentration of the contaminants in the air. Indeed, many industrial workplaces are monitored continuously for a variety of contaminants. (Regular, if not continuous, monitoring is necessary to adequately capture variations in airborne contaminant levels.) Unfortunately, routine monitoring of asbestos in buildings is an expensive and often impractical proposition.

Although the method for measuring asbestos required by OSHA for workplace settings where levels are expected to be elevated (<u>phase contrast microscopy</u>-PCM) is relatively inexpensive and thus practical for routine use, it is not an accurate gauge of asbestos levels in other settings.
The reasons are two-fold.
1. PCM measures fibers in general, not just asbestos fibers
2. PCM cannot detect thin fibers (less than about 0.25 <u>micrometers</u> in diameter) which comprise the majority of airborne asbestos fibers in buildings with ACM.

Thus, PCM measurements will be influenced by a variety of nonasbestos fibers and may miss high levels of asbestos if the fibers are thin.

A better method for measuring asbestos is <u>transmission electron microscopy</u> (TEM). TEM can distinguish between asbestos and nonasbestos fibers, and can "see" extremely thin fibers. But TEM is expensive ($75 to $200 a sample). This means that a properly designed, comprehensive air monitoring program (several sampling locations in the building, and measurements made at least every few months and under a variety of conditions) could cost tens of thousands of dollars annually.

For these reasons, EPA does not recommend air sampling as a "stand alone" assessment method, and the AHERA Rule does not mention air monitoring for a assessment purposes. Instead, the condition, locations, and accessibility of ACBM should be used to judge the likelihood of fiber release and subsequent exposure of building workers. Some building owners may still wish to conduct periodic air monitoring for airborne asbestos. They reason that even if low recorded levels may give a false sense of security, high levels of fibers point to potentially hazardous conditions. Consequently, building inspectors and management planners may wish to become conversant in air monitoring methodology.

PHYSICAL ASSESSMENT

Various methods have been proposed and used to assess the tendency of ACM found in a particular location to release fibers and thus to increase the potential for exposure of workers and building occupants. Some methods employ numerical scoring schemes often referred to as "algorithms". The advantage of a numerical scheme is that scores (e.g., 0-100) are automatically produced which can then be used to define the degree of hazard or potential for exposure, and the urgency for response action. However, EPA has studied the use of algorithms and concluded that they may not be reliable estimators of hazard or exposure potential. Rather, they tend to give the assessment process a false sense of precision.

Various non-numerical or quasi-numerical approaches have been developed for conducting physical assessments of ACM. Most employ many of the same factors used in numerical scoring schemes. The difference is that evaluating each factor leads to a categorical outcome (e.g., "present/absent", "high/medium/low") instead of a numerical scores.

The various approaches differ primarily in how the assessment information is formatted and displayed for subsequent decision-making. Some use simple tabular displays or a decision tree to aid in selecting appropriate response actions for various combinations of assessments results. The AHERA Rule does not specify any particular type of assessment method. Any method can be used as long as the required response actions are selected. In other words, any assessment method can be used as long as the assessed material is placed in the correct category of damage and potential for damage by the building inspector, and the response action (s) allowed by the AHERA are recommended by the management planner and selected by the <u>Local Education Agency</u> (LEA).

Appendix H-1 describes one assessment method in detail and how it is used to meet AHERA requirements. Appendix H-2 summarized three different assessment methods. References are provided for those wishing to obtain more information.

IDENTIFYING FUNCTIONAL SPACES

According to the AHERA Rule, the basic unit for collecting assessment data is the "functional space". Functional spaces are spatially distinct units within a building and sometimes contain different populations of building occupants. For example, a classroom is a functional space because it is enclosed and separate from the rest of the building and contains one or more groups of students and teachers. Similarly, a boiler room would be a functional space containing custodial and maintenance workers. A corridor and an auditorium are other examples; in these case, the relevant population would be all students, faculty, and staff or office workers. Pipe chases, air shafts, and air plenums are also functional spaces although they do not contain populations. The list of building areas in Section G(Exhibit G-1) can be used as a guide to identify functional spaces in a particular building. Considerable latitude is allowed to the building inspector under AHERA. For example, long corridors could be divided into separate spaces if the inspector finds it useful in identifying important distinctions in the conditions and/or disturbance potential of suspect material.

Several functional spaces may comprise a homogeneous sampling area. For example, an entire floor comprised of many classrooms or offices and a corridor could be a single homogenous area for purposes of bulk sampling. That is to say, the same suspect materials could have been sprayed on all ceilings or on beams above suspended ceilings or wrapped around pipes in every room throughout the floor. A few sites for collecting bulk samples would be located randomly (or by convenience) throughout the floor whereas the material in each individual functional space would be assessed. This means that the number of separate assessments is likely to exceed the number of sampling areas, at least for surfacing material. Functional spaces with different types of suspect materials may present the opposite situation. A boiler room, for example, may have a variety of thermal insulation in addition to surfacing material. Several sampling areas thus would be used in this single functional space. This should not be confusing as long as one understands that homogeneous areas are used for sampling suspect material and functional spaces are used for assessing suspected material.

Where several different types of homogeneous sampling areas are found in a single functional space, the physical assessment of the area may be a composite assessment. Surfacing materials are assessed separately from thermal system insulation. However, different types of thermal insulation (e.g. pipe wrap, elbow insulation, boiler block) in one space are assessed as a single unit.

Every functional space which contains suspect material should be assessed under AHERA. However, large buildings may contain many repeating functional units with the same type of suspect material in the same condition and with the same potential for disturbance (e.g., hotel rooms, apartments, classrooms). In this case, all similar units could be grouped together and identified as a single functional space, and a representative number of the repeating units could be used for the physical assessment. If such an approach is used, selection of at least 20% is recommended (i.e., one of every five separate rooms in the collective functional space should be selected and the suspect material therein assessed). The overall assessment of the suspect material in the collective functional space would then be the average of the assessments in each sample rom (all of which should be roughly the same).

Note that only rooms or spaces with material in the same condition and with the same potential for disturbance should be grouped together. If otherwise identical rooms do not meet these conditions, they should not be included in the same functional space. For example, if 10 classrooms in an elementary school all have acoustical plaster ceilings but two have been damaged, two separate functional spaces could be identified—one for the eight rooms in good condition and one for the two with damaged plaster. Likewise, classrooms should not be grouped together with spaces where the potential for disturbance might differ (e.g., corridors or rest rooms), even if the suspect material is the same and in the same condition.

A unique number should be assigned to each functional space assessed. Consider using existing identifiers (e.g., room numbers). For unnumbered areas such as corridors, rest rooms, auditoriums, and vestibules, simple codes could be used. Letter codes such as those in Exhibit G-1 could be combined with numbers reflecting specific floor locations. For example, MR5 would be the mechanical room on the fifth floor, and RR-B-2 would be rest room #2 in the basement. Using this or a similar coding scheme, record functional space numbers on the floor plans. Functional spaces such as air plenums and mechanical chases should be sketched on the floor plans, or, if this is confusing, on attached sheets.

CATEGORIZING ASSESSED MATERIAL

The results of the physical assessment must be recorded as specified in the AHERA Rule. This means placing all homogenous material assessed in each functional space into one of the seven condition/potential for disturbance categories discussed earlier (see page H-3 for a list of the 7 categories), and illustrated in Exhibit H-4. Note that current conditions are the primary consideration when making the category assignments. That is, categories #1-4 are reserved for material which is damaged or significantly damaged. Only if the material is in good condition is potential for disturbance a consideration (categories #5-7). Note also that the damage and significant damage categories are combined for thermal system insulation and for friable miscellaneous materials.

RECORDING INSPECTION ASSESSMENT RESULTS

The results of the physical assessment of known or assumed materials should be recorded, perhaps on a form like the one in Exhibit H-5. Note that this form includes all types and categories of ACBM—known or assumed, friable or nonfriable, assessed or not assessed. Note also, that material that does not need to be assessed (nonfriable surfacing and miscellaneous ACBM) still needs a brief description of its general condition. Finally, the cause of damage to any ACBM needs to be identified.

EXHIBIT H-1
SUMMARY OF AHERA INSPECTION, SAMPLING, AND ASSESSMENT REQUIREMENT

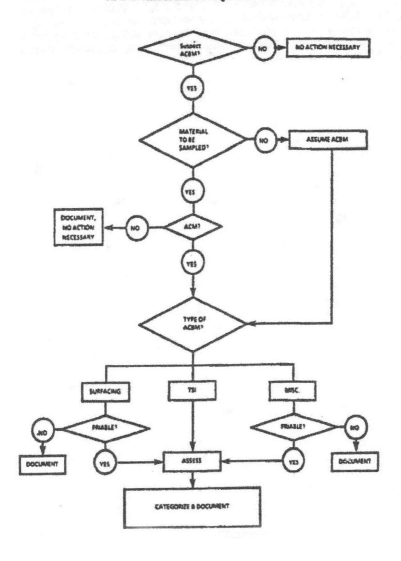

EXHIBIT H-2

INSPECTION, SAMPLING, AND ASSESSMENT REQUIREMENTS UNDER AHERA

Activity	Surfacing Material		Thermal System Insulation	Miscellaneous Material	
	Friable	Nonfriable	Friable/Nonfriable*	Friable	Nonfriable
Inspection and Documentation	Yes	Yes	Yes	Yes	Yes
Sampling	Between 3 and 7 random samples **	As determined by an accredited inspector***	-At least 3 random samples of most TSI -1 sample of patched TSI if it is <6 linear or square feet -As determined by an accd. Inspector for mudded joints and fittings	As determined by an accredited inspector	
Assessment	Yes	No	Yes	Yes	No

*Thermal System Insulation shall be treated as nonfriable unless it is damaged. However, AHERA still requires that TSI be assessed during inspections.

**Minimum based on square footage.

***An Inspector may want to consider increasing the number of samples collected from this material, since asbestos content of nonfriable surfacing material may vary.

EXHIBIT H-3
ASSUMED ACBM LOCATION FORM

Building: _____

Location		Type of Material				General Condition (Describe)
Function al Space No.	Floor	SM	TSI	Misc.	Describe	

Note: SM is surfacing material and TSI is thermal system insulation

Inspector: _____

Date: _____

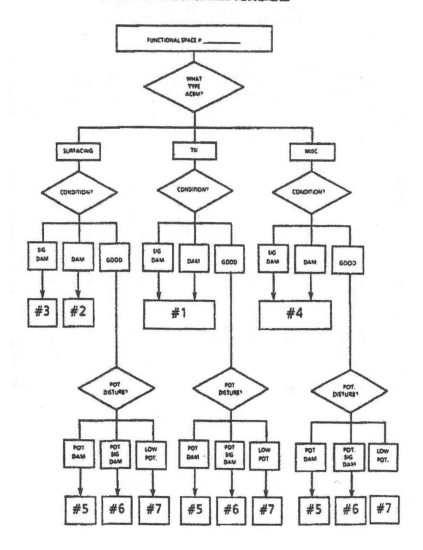

EXHIBIT H-4
CATEGORIZING ASSESSED MATERIAL

EXHIBIT H-5

EXAMPLE FORMAT FOR SUMMARIZING SAMPLING AND ASSESSMENT RESULTS

ACBM locations		ACBM Characteristics				Assessment Results			
Homogenous Area No.	Function Space No.	Type	Friable/ Non-friable	% ablation	Amount of material	Condition	Potential disturbance	AHE RA Category	Reason for Damage

ASSESSING THE POTENTIAL FOR DISTURBANCE

The likelihood that the suspect material could be disturbed in the future is related to (1) the frequency with which service workers need to work near or building occupants are in the vicinity of the material, (2) its location with respect to sources of vibration, and (3) the potential for air erosion. Exhibit H-1-5 defines each of these factors and provides guidance for evaluating them in the field. Note that the factors are evaluated differently depending on whether service workers or other building occupants are the ones likely to contact the material.

The results of evaluating the factors in Exhibit H-1-5 are then used to classify the material with respect to its potential for disturbance. The categories are: potential for significant damage, potential for damage, and low potential. The high category corresponds to "potential for significant damage", and the moderate category corresponds to "potential for damage", in the AHERA terminology.

The classification scheme is illustrated in Exhibit H-1-6. As shown, if any one of these three factors (frequency of potential contact, influence of vibration, and potential for air erosion) is determined to be high, then the level of potential disturbance is "potential for significant damage" as defined in AHERA, regardless of ratings for the other two criteria. Similarly, if none of the three criteria is assessed as high but at least one has a rating of "moderate" then the level of potential disturbance is designated "potential for damage" as defined in AHERA. If all three criteria are rated low, then the overall rating is "low potential". Note, that AHERA does not refer specifically to material in good condition or with low potential for disturbance.

OTHER DATA IMPORTANT FOR ESTIMATING EXPOSURE POTENTIAL

Once asbestos fibers are released from ACBM, the degree to which they pose a danger to building workers and occupants depends on their concentration in the air at locations where people are present. Understanding the building's HVAC system is important to understanding the transport of released fibers. Any time fibers are released into the ventilation air stream they have the potential to be transported to occupied spaces. Thus, whether or not the ACBM is located in the air plenum should be noted. Location in a supply air plenum is more significant than in a return plenum since the distance of the transport to the occupied space is usually shorter and dilution by makeup air is less significant.

The total amount of suspect material in damaged or deteriorated condition may also affect the level of asbestos in the air. The amount of material can be calculated from the estimated percent of damage and the estimated amount of material present.

Finally, additional information may be useful for other purposes. For example, the number of people in the building is needed to apply for EPA grants and loans for ACM abatement under the Asbestos in School Hazard Abatement Act (ASHAA).

RECORDING ASSESSMENT DATA

All of the data discussed above should be collected in a systematic manner. Exhibit H-1-7 is a data form that could be used for this purpose.

The form should be filled in as follows:
- Fill in the building name, functional space number, and description of the location in the building. Note the type of area as well, including details such as whether it is a supply or return air plenum.
- Identify the type and amount of suspect material being assessed and describe it. Note: Where various types of material are present in a single functional space (e.g., fireproofing, acoustical plaster, and pipe wrap in a classroom), a separate form should be filled out for each material.
- Calculate the approximate amount of material by estimating the square feet of surfacing or miscellaneous material or the linear feet of pipe wrap, the number of pipe elbows, and the square feet of other types of thermal insulation.
- Estimate the extent and type of damage/deterioration and describe it.
- Using the rating scheme summarized in Exhibits H1-1 and H1-2, rate the overall condition of the material.
- Using the potential for disturbance rating scheme summarize din Exhibit H-1-5, rate the frequency of potential contact, the influence of vibration and the potential for air erosion. Describe the conditions observed in arriving at your rating.
- Using the classification in Exhibit H-1-6, rate the overall potential for disturbance.
- Add any additional comments that may be useful to the Management Planner in developing a plan to manage the ACBM.

EXHIBIT H-1-1
CLASSIFYING THE CONDITION OF SUSPECT MATERIAL SURFACING AND MISCELLANEOUS MATERIAL

"Significantly Damaged"

Material with <u>one or more</u> of the following characteristics:
- The surface crumbling or blistered over at least one tenth of the surface if the damage is evenly distributed (one quarter if the damage is localized).
- One tenth (one quarter, if localized) of material hanging from the surface, deteriorated, or showing adhesive failure.
- Water stains, gouges, or mars over at least one tenth of the surface if the damage is evenly distributed (one quarter if the damage is localized).

Accumulation of powder, dust, or debris similar in appearance to the suspect material on surfaces beneath the material can be used as confirmatory evidence.

"Damaged"

Material with the following characteristic:
- The surface crumbling, blistered, water-stained, gouged, marred, or otherwise abraded over less than one tenth of the surface if the damage is evenly distributed (one quarter if the damage is localized).

Accumulation of powder, dust, or debris similar in appearance to the suspect material on surfaces beneath the material can be used as confirmatory evidence.

Good Condition

Material with no visible damage or deterioration, or showing only very limited damage or deterioration.

AHERA DEFINITION OF SIGNIFICANTLY DAMAGED FRIABLE SURFACING MISCELLANEOUS ACM

"Friable surfacing miscellaneous ACM is a functional space where damage is extensive and severe." Note, the Preamble to the AHERA rule makes reference to 10 and 25 percent damage as a means of distinguishing significantly damaged from damaged ACBM.

AHERA DEFINITION OF DAMAGED FRIABLE SURFACING MISCELLANEOUS ACM

"Friable surfacing miscellaneous ACM which has deteriorated or sustained physical injury such that the internal structure (cohesion) of the material is inadequate or, if applicable, which has delaminated such that the bond to the substrate (adhesion) is inadequate or which for any other reason lacks fiber cohesion or adhesion qualities. Such damage or deterioration may be illustrated by the separation of the ACM into layers; separation of ACM from the substrate; flaking, blistering, or crumbling of ACM surface; water damage; significant or repeated water stains, scrapes, gouges, mars or other signs of physical injury on the ACM. Asbestos debris originating from the ACBM in question may also indicate damage."

EXHIBIT H-1-2
CLASSIFYING THE CONDITION OF SUSPECT MATERIAL
THERMAL SYSTEM INSULATION

"Significantly Damaged"

Material with <u>one or more</u> of the following characteristics:

- Missing jackets on at least one tenth of the piping or equipment.
- Crushed or heavily gouged or punctured insulation on at least one tenth of pipe runs/risers, boiler, tank, duct, etc. if the damage is evenly distributed (one quarter if the damage is localized).
-

Accumulation of powder, dust, or debris similar in appearance to the suspect material on surfaces beneath the pipe/boiler/tank/duct, etc. can be used as confirmatory evidence.

"Damaged"

Material with <u>one or more</u> of the following characteristics:

- A few water stains or less than one tenth of the insulation with missing jackets
- Crushed insulation or water stains, gouges, punctures, or mars on up to one tenth of the insulation if the damage is evenly distributed (or up to one quarter if the damage is localized).

Accumulation of powder, dust, or debris similar in appearance to the suspect material on surfaces beneath the pipe/boiler/tank/etc. can be used as confirmatory evidence.

Good Condition

Material with no visible damage or deterioration, or showing only very limited damage or deterioration.

AHERA DEFINITION OF DAMAGED OR SIGNIFICANTLY DAMAGED THERMAL SYSTEM INSULATION

"Thermal system insulation ACM on pipes, boilers, tanks, ducts, and other thermal system insulation equipment which has lost its structural integrity, or its covering, in whole or in part, is crushed, water-stained, gouged, punctured, missing, or not intact such that it is not able to contain fibers. Damage may be further illustrated by occasional punctures, gouges, or other signs of physical injury to ACM; occasional water damage on the protective coverings/jackets; or exposed ACM ends or joints. Asbestos debris, originating from the ACBM in question may also indicate damage."

Note: The AHERA Rule has only one category of damage: "Damaged or significantly damaged".

EXHIBIT H-1-3

REPRESENTATION OF TEN PERCENT DISTRIBUTED DAMAGE

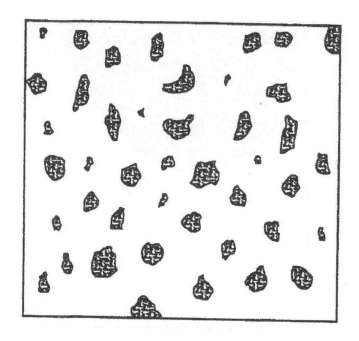

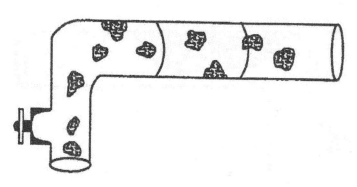

EXHIBIT H-1-4

REPRESENTATION OF TWENTY FIVE PERCENT LOCALIZED DAMAGE

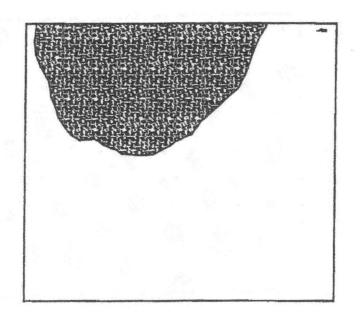

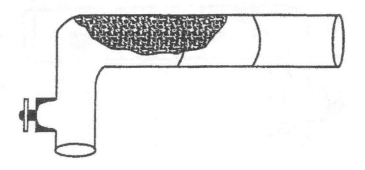

EXHIBIT H-1-5
FACTORS TO BE USED IN DETERMINING THE POTENTIAL FOR
DISTURBANCE OF SUSPECT MATERIAL

POTENTIAL FOR CONTACT WITH THE MATERIAL
High:
- Service workers work in the vicinity of the material more than once per week or
- The material is in a public area (e.g., hallway, corridor, auditorium) and accessible to building occupants.

Moderate:
- Service workers work in the vicinity of the material once per month to once per week or
- The material is in a room or office and accessible to the occupants

Low:
- Service workers work in the vicinity of the material less than once per month or
- The material is visible but not within reach of building occupants.

INFLUENCE OF VIBRATION
High:
- Loud motors or engines present (e.g., some fan rooms), or
- Intrusive noises or easily sensed vibrations (e.g., major airports, a major highway).

Moderate:
- Motors or engines present but not obtrusive (e.g., ducts vibrating but no fan in the area), or
- Occasional loud sounds (e.g., a music room).

Low/None:
- None of the above

POTENTIAL FOR AIR EROSION
High:
- High velocity air (e.g., elevator shaft, fan room)

Moderate:
- Noticeable movement of air (e.g., air shaft, ventilator, air stream).

Low/None:
- None of the above.

EXHIBIT H-1-6
CLASSIFICATION OF THE POTENTIAL FOR DISTURBANCE

Potential for disturbance	Frequency of potential contact	Influence of vibration	Potential for air erosion
"Potential for significant damage"	Any High Value		
"Potential for Damage"	Any Moderate Value		
Low Potential	All Low Values		

AHERA DEFINITIONS

Potential Damage
1.   Friable ACBM is in an area regularly used by building occupants, including maintenance personnel, in the course of their normal activities.
2.   There are indications that there is a reasonable likelihood that the material or its covering will become damaged, deteriorated, or delaminated due to factors such as changes in building use, changes in O&M practices, changes in occupancy, or recurrent damage.

Potential for Significant Damage

Same as potential damage, plus:
3.   The material is subject to major or continuing disturbance, due to factors including but not limited to, accessibility or, under certain circumstances, vibration or air erosion.

EXHIBIT H-1-7
RECORDING FORM FOR PHYSICAL ASSESSMENT DATA

Building: _____

Functional Space No._____Type:_____Location:_____

Type of suspect material:_____Surfacing,_____TSI_____Misc.
  Description:_____
  _____

Approximate Amount of Material (linear, square, or cubic ft.):_____

Condition

Percent Damage:_____%, _____Localized, _____Distributed

Type of Damage:_____Deterioration,_____Water, _____Physical
Description: _____
_____

Overall rating: _____Good, _____Damaged, _____Sig. Damaged

Potential for Disturbance

Frequency of Potential Contact: _____High, _____Moderate, _____Low
Description: _____
_____

Influence of Vibration: _____High, _____Moderate, _____Low
Description: _____
_____

Potential for Air Erosion: _____High, _____Moderate, _____Low
Description: _____
_____

Rate Potential for: ___Damage, ____Sig. Damage, ____Minimal or No Damage
Comments: _____
_____

Signed: _____Date: _____

Inspector Accreditation Number: _____

APPENDIX H-2
ALTERNATIVE HAZARD ASSESSMENT METHODS

A wide variety of methods have been used to assess existing or potential hazards posed by asbestos-containing materials (ACM) and which identify the appropriate methods for corrective action.

Three approaches, with examples (parentheses), are:
1. Table (EPA Purple Book)
2. Decision Trees (EPA Draft Assessment Guidance Document and the British Pink Book)
3. Matrix stratification (Entek)

A few common characteristics are worth noting:
- Condition of the material is a key criteria, if not the key criteria, in each method.
- Most methods differentiate between at least two levels of damage, occasionally requires removal.
- Accessibility is the second most prominent criteria

Numerical scoring schemes (or "algorithms") are not discussed, since EPA does not recommend their use (see page H-7).

EPA PURPLE BOOK (Table)

Comments

- Provides separate analysis for three material types: surfacing material, pipe and boiler insulation (thermal system insulation) and other (miscellaneous) types of ACM.
- Discusses need, timing and recommends methods of abatement for each type.
- Provides assessment tables for surfacing material and pipe and boiler insulation
- Classifies homogeneous sampling areas of either surfacing material or pipe and boiler insulation into six general categories given two key characteristics:
    - Current condition of ACM (good, minor damage, poor)
    - Potential for future damage, disturbance, or erosion (low, high)
- Provides comparative analysis of abatement methods.

Observations

Simple to use, but highly qualitative. Allows flexibility in choosing a response; identifies removal as having "the widest applicability" and "the only truly permanent solution." Unit of analysis is homogeneous sampling area. Differentiates between surfacing material and thermal system insulation, in that former is less amenable to repair and less localized. Does not provide manner for relative ranking of individual projects/hazards with categories.

EPA DRAFT ASSESSMENT DOCUMENT (Decision Tree)

Comments
- Provides separate analyses for surfacing material and thermal system insulation.
- Offers detailed discussion of three key factors for assessing potential exposure to asbestos: The condition of the ACM, disturbance (existing and potential, which includes accessibility) and air flow.
- Classifies damage as:
  - Significant (10% scattered, 24% localized)
  - Moderate (up to 10% scattered, 25% localized)
  - Good condition ("No visible....or showing only very limited" damage)
- Results in 8 prioritized response action categories, ranging from removal ASAP (RA1) to continue O&M until NESHAP removal, by renovation or demolition, is required (RA8).
- Decision process flows as follows:
  - Friable? If so, assess condition. If not, O&M.
  - Condition? If significant damage, isolate area and remove ASAP, if good, O&M, but assess disturbance i.e., potential. If moderate damage, assess disturbance.
  - Disturbance level? If high, remove ASAP or reduce potential for disturbance. If moderate or low, assess airflow
  - Air flow? Four prioritized categories, depending upon disturbance level and presence of air flow

Observations

Developed as guidance by EPA, in response to requests form schools and other building owners for more specificity than provided in Purple Book. Modified by panel of experts. Fairly rigid structure. Provides priority listing by the 8 categories. Unit of analysis is homogeneous sampling area for surfacing material; system for thermal system insulation—larger units than other schemes. Intended to help owners recognize economies of scale and long-term considerations.

Reference: D. Keyes, B. Price, and J. Chesson, "Guidance for Assessing and Managing Exposure to Asbestos in Buildings," Draft, November 7, 1986. Section 2 (pp. 5-22), Section 3 (pp. 24-40), and Trees, p. 26 and 39.

BRITISH PINK BOOK (Decision Tree)

Comments
- Highly qualitative discussion of assessment, outlining the:
  o Potential for fiber release
  o Type of material (i.e., sprayed asbestos, etc.)
  o Integrity of the material (condition)
  o Position of the material (potential for disturbance)
- Proposes separate decision trees for each of three types of asbestos-containing material:
  o Sprayed asbestos (sprayed-on surfacing material) and lagging (thermal system insulation).
  o Asbestos insulating board
  o Asbestos cement products
- Decision process flows as follows
  o Contain asbestos? If so, assess condition. If not, record as non-asbestos material
  o Good condition? If so, management (O&M). If not, identify material type.
  o Sprayed asbestos or lagging? If so, to Chart 2. (If not, to other appropriate charts).
  o Readily repairable? If so, repair. If not, assess accessibility.
  o Damage extensive? If so, is there loos friable material? If not, seal or enclose.
  o Loos friable material? If so, is enclosure feasible? If not, seal or enclose?
  o Enclosure feasible? If so, enclose. If not, remove.
  o Management (O&M) is required for all material not removed.

Observations

Highly qualitative, but simple to use. Limits flexibility of response. Heavy reliance on proper management (O&M). Appears to reserve removal for only those cases where other methods ((O&M), encapsulation, enclosure) are first ruled out as inappropriate. Licensed contractor performs abatement activity.

Reference: Department of the Environment, Asbestos Materials in Buildings, Second Edition, 1986. Chapter 4 (pp. 16-18), Annex 3 (pp. 38-45).

MATRIX STRATIFICATION (Matrix)

Comments
- Proposes integrated survey of structure and suspect materials; inventory utilizing specific classifications of survey data; and a summary matrix of the inventory for assessment.
- Utilizes three basic inventory variables for matrix:
  o Accessibility, with 4 dimensions: Yes or no in restricted area (boiler room) or non-restricted area (classroom or hallway)
  o Condition, with three or four dimensions (intact, minor damage, moderate damage, severe damage) depending on type of material and other factors
  o Quantity of material (in precise linear, area or unit measurements).
- Places quantity of material as unit in cells.
- Matches response actions with conditions. For example, for thermal system insulation matrix:
  o Intact, monitor
  o Minor damage, patch
  o Moderate, cover (repair)
  o Severe, remove
- Allows addition or deletion of cells, as appropriate (Repair dimension would often be dropped for surfacing material.

Observations

Provides some prioritization and allows characterization of the overall pictures. Dynamic. Facilitates cost analysis. Not project or area based (unit of analysis is smaller measure). Computer application. Appears more sophisticated than tables or trees. Heavy weight on accessibility factors. Reliance on engineering factors and definitions (i.e., does lack of "design failure" necessarily rule out health risk?).

Reference: Entek Environmental and Technical Services, Inc. evironmental regulations.

INTRODUCTION

This section covers all aspects of collecting <u>bulk samples</u> of suspect materials. Following the discussion of a sampling plan for surfacing materials,

this section proceeds to address sampling plans for thermal system insulation and other suspect materials. Also included are procedures for collecting samples, a description of bulk sample analysis, and a general discussion on laboratory <u>quality assurance</u> (QA) programs.

PLANNING AND DESIGNING THE SAMPLING OPERATION

SURFACING MATERIALS

The following discussion is based largely on a portion of the EPA guidance document, <u>Asbestos in Buildings: Simplified Sampling Scheme for Friable Surfacing Materials</u>.

IDENTIFYING SAMPLING AREAS

Group friable surfacing material into "homogeneous" sampling areas. A <u>homogeneous sampling area</u> contains friable material that is uniform in texture, color, date of application, and appears identical in very other respect. Materials installed at different times belong to different homogeneous sampling areas. If there is any reason to suspect that materials might be different even though they appear uniform, assign them to separate homogeneous sampling areas. For example, material in different wings of a building, or different floors, or in special areas such as cafeterias, matching shops, band rooms, etc. should be assigned to separate homogeneous sampling areas unless there is good reason to believe that the material is identical throughout.

In a large multi-story building (more than 10 stories), a separate homogeneous sampling area for each floor may not be necessary. If the material appears identical on every floor, several floors can be grouped into one homogeneous sampling area. Do not group floors if it is known that the material was applied at different times, or if there is some other reason or suspect that the material might not be homogeneous. The selection of homogeneous sampling area is a subjective process. When in doubt, assign materials to separate homogeneous sampling areas.

PREPARATION OF DIAGRAMS

For each homogeneous sampling area, use a prepared diagram or prepare a diagram approximately to scale showing all friable materials in the sampling area. Where the suspect material is only on horizontal surfaces, a to-scale floor plan could be used. An example of a diagram is shown on Exhibit I-1. The homogeneous sampling area diagram should include:

- An identification number
- Brief description of the sampling area
- Area dimensions and scale
- Name and telephone number of the asbestos program manager (the "designated person" according to AHERA)
- Name of inspector and date of inspection
- Name of person preparing the diagram and date prepared

If the homogeneous sampling area contains areas of friable material that are not adjacent (for example, homogeneous areas on consecutive floors of a building), sketch each separate area and place all sketches on the same graph as close together as possible. The sampling area may contain areas that are not in one plane; for example, a ceiling and a wall with the same type of friable material. In this case, sketch each flat surface and place the sketches on the same graph as close together as possible. The sampling area diagrams should be retained as part of the building owner's permanent asbestos program file.

NUMBER OF SAMPLES

A minimum of nine bulk samples per homogeneous sampling area is recommended. With nine samples, the likelihood of detecting asbestos when it is present is very high. Cost or other constraints may limit the number of samples that can be collected. If nine samples cannot be collected, use the following table to determine the minimum number as required by the AHERA Rule. This number depends on the size of the homogeneous sampling area. In a very small (much less than 1,000 square feet) sampling area such as a closet, take three samples rather than the full nine.

Size of the Homogeneous Sampling Area	Recommended Number of Samples to be Collected	Minimum Number of Samples to be Collected
Less than 1,000 ft^2	9	3
Between 1,000 & 5,000 ft^2	9	5
Greater than 5,000 ft^2	9	7

SELECTION OF SAMPLE LOCATIONS

In this sampling scheme, sample locations are selected so that they are representative of the homogeneous sampling area with regard to the material present and its potential asbestos content. When nine samples are collected, they are distributed evenly over the sampling area. If few than nine samples are collected, they are distributed evenly over the sampling area. If fewer than nine samples are collected, a random sampling scheme is used to determine their location.

SECTION I: BULK SAMPLING OF SUSPECT MATERIALS

Choosing sample locations according to personal judgment produces samples which may not be representative and can lead to a wrong decision about the presence of absence of asbestos. The sampling scheme described here avoids this problem and controls the frequency of mistakes.

Divide the homogeneous sampling area does not easily fit into a rectangular shape, parts of the grid might not be in the sampling area. This is not a problem in most cases. If, however, a large part of the grid falls outside the homogeneous sampling area (for example, if the sample area is L-shaped), it is advisable to divide the sampling area into two or more separate sampling areas, each of which is approximately rectangular, and select sample locations by applying the sampling scheme to each sampling area.

For greatest coverage, one sample from each of the nine grid regions should be collected. If fewer samples are to be collected, the diagrams in Exhibit I-3 show which subareas to use in order to follow a random sampling scheme. For the first area you intend to sample, number the nine subareas as shown for Sampling Area #1 in Exhibit I-3. If three samples are needed, take them from the subareas marked 1,2,3,4, and 5, and so on. Take samples from approximately the center of a subarea or as close as possible to the center if accessibility, presence of light fixtures, etc. make the center location impractical. If a subarea is specified that falls entirely outside the sampling area, use the next specified subarea instead. For example, if subarea three falls outside the sampling area, take the third sample from subarea 4.

For very irregular-shaped areas, the homogeneous sampling area may be divided into none subareas of approximately equal size that do not necessarily form a rectangular grid. The diagrams in Exhibit I-3 will then need to be adapted to specific situation. Exhibit I-4 shows an example of a Y-shaped sampling area that was divided into nine subareas of equal size. The first diagram of Exhibit I-2 was adapted accordingly to number the subareas. When adapting sampling diagrams, retain the order of the numbered subareas from left to right and top to bottom whenever possible.

For each sampling area, use a new diagram in Exhibit I-3. If you have more than 18 sampling areas, start again at the top of Exhibit I-3 (Sampling Area #1) to determine sampling locations for Sampling Area 19.

IDENTIFICATION OF SAMPLES

Assign a unique sample ID number to each bulk sample collected. This ID number will be on the sampling container when it goes to the laboratory for analysis. Record the ID number and the sample location on the sampling area diagram and also on a data sheet (see Administrative Supplies below). This must be done carefully so that there is no uncertainty about the location and identity of each sample. Make sure that no two samples have the same ID number. Non-sequential numbers should be used to prevent the laboratories from knowing which samples come from the same sampling areas or the same buildings. This "blind" procedure helps prevent bias on the part of the analyst since there is no temptation to assume that the next sample will be similar to the previous one. On the other hand, non0sequential ID numbers make organizing the analytical results by homogeneous sampling area much more difficult. Perhaps an alpha code which identifies, by letter, a building and/or area combined with non-sequential numerical scheme is best.

EXAMPLE

The sampling procedure is illustrated by this example. A school was visually inspected for friable materials. The Activity Center Annex was found to contain friable ceiling materials. All materials were believed to be the same, and thus comprise one sampling area.

Approximate room dimensions were obtained by pacing, and diagrammed as shown in Exhibit I-1.

There were not enough funds for nine samples to be collected in every homogeneous sampling area. Therefore, the minimum number, based on area, was calculated. The total area of friable materials is 10,080 ft^2 (square feet) as calculated by:

$$Area = (60' \times 90') + (12' \times 90') + (60' \times 60')$$

$$= 10,080 \ ft^2$$

Since this area is greater than 5,000 square feet, a minimum of seven samples should be collected. This number was taken from the list appearing earlier in this section—The Number of Samples to be Collected from Each Sampling Area.

The sampling area diagram was divided into nine subareas. Assuming this is the second sampling area to be sampled, the second diagram of Exhibit I-3 is used. The region marked "6" in the diagram does not fall within the sampling area. Therefore, the regions marked I-5 and 7 and 8 were used to obtain several samples. These seven locations were marked on the sampling area diagram as shown in Exhibit I-2. Each sampling location was assigned a unique, non-systematic sample ID number and this number was marked on the sampling area diagram. A quality control sample was also collected in subsection 4 immediately adjacent to the original sample. This sample was also given a unique, non-systematic sample ID number.

THERMAL SYSTEM INSULATION

The concept of homogeneous sampling areas applies equally well to thermal system insulation (TSAR) as to surfacing material. The major difference is that insulation on thermal systems is likely to be much more varied than materials on surfaces. A "typical" building or industrial facility may contain multiple insulated pipe runs from any combination of the following major categories:

- Hot water supply and/or return
- Cold water supply
- Chilled water supply
- Steam supply and/or return (watch for different pressure/temperature steam lines)
- Roof or system drain
- Chemical or waste transport

Each of these systems may have been installed at different times and insulated with different materials. Therefore, it is best to first identify the building system in question and use this information in conjunction with the physical appearance of the insulation to delineate homogeneous sampling areas.

Each "system" may be composed of a variety of materials. For example, the following list contains 9 different types of thermal insulation:

- Corrugated cardboard-type pipe wrap
- White chalky pipe wrap
- Fibrous glass insulation covering a pipe wrap of unknown characteristics
- Cementitious "mud" around pipe fittings
- Hard, canvas-wrapped insulation on pipe elbows
- Block insulation on boilers
- White batt insulation on boiler breeching
- Black batt insulation inside ducts
- Rope around pipe sleeves in ceiling and floor slabs

Each of these insulation types should be considered a separate component of the system, and a separate homogeneous area for sampling purposes. Fibrous glass, foam glass rubber, and Styrofoam are not suspect materials. Note, however, that they may cover up ACM.

The number of samples and the sample locations will depend on local circumstances. At least three samples must be collected from each homogeneous area of thermal system insulation. For long pipe runs or risers, more samples should be taken, especially if the piping extends to more than one functional space. Pay special attention to any change in the appearance of the insulation on long pipe runs. This would indicate a possible change insulation type and the need to delineate a new sampling area. The AHERA Rule requires at least three random samples for thermal insulation. Exceptions are: (1) small sections (less than 6 linear or square feet) of patched insulation (at least one sample), and (2) areas of insulating cement (the number of samples to be determined by the Building Inspector).

Consideration should be given to the amount and extent of damage to TSI which may occur as a result of bulk sampling. Some building owners may not want "destructive sampling" conducted on their TSI which may be in good condition.

The AHERA regulations require random sampling, which may dictate that samples will be collected from TSI in good condition. The building owner and building inspector should decide prior to conducting the survey whether sample collection and the associated damage which will result is necessary, or if assuming the insulation contains asbestos and maintaining its condition is best. Convenience sampling, or collecting samples from exposed asbestos or damaged areas, may be more appropriate for non-AHERA inspections, such as those performed for environmental site assessments or non-school buildings.

MISCELLANEOUS MATERIALS

Miscellaneous suspect materials are, for the most part, nonfriable (ceilings tiles are an exception). As such, bulk sampling is typically more difficult and destructive. EPA does not recommend sampling these materials. Instead, they should be identified as suspect and documented as such in permanent records.

Some building owners wish to have miscellaneous materials sampled and analyzed anyway. Ceiling and floor tiles are probably the most frequently sampled types of materials in the miscellaneous category. If sampling is desired, try to identify separate homogeneous areas just as you would for surfacing material and thermal insulation. (You will probably find that many different types, colors, and vintages of both floor and ceiling tile can be found in a building.) Then collect convenience samples in inconspicuous locations.
A building inspector may choose to follow the sampling protocol developed for surfacing material when sampling miscellaneous material. Very hard materials like asbestos-cement wallboard should not be sampled. Not only is sampling needlessly destructive and hazardous, asbestos-0cement wallboard can easily be identified.

COLLECTING BULK SAMPLES

PERSONAL PROTECTIVE EQUIPMENT

Since inhalation of asbestos fibers which might be released during hundreds of inspection and sampling jobs may pose a serious health hazard, the use of personal protective equipment by building inspectors is crucial during the sampling process. As a minimum level of protection, inspectors should wear a respirator, either a full or half-face mask with high efficiency disposable filter cartridges. (See Section J for more information on respiratory protection.) Full face masks will also prevent eye irritation from dust, fibers, and debris released during the sampling operation. Disposable clothing should be worn during sampling if the sampling operation is likely to dislodge pieces of suspect material or if the environment is extremely dust (e.g., crawl space, dirty mechanical room). Hearing protection should be used if a building inspector must spend a considerable amount of time in a mechanical room, processing plant, or similar location where operating machinery produces significant noise. Inspectors should have plastic bags, twisters, and labels with them to handle the disposal of cartridges, protective clothing, wet cloths, and debris. These waste materials should be stored pending survey results. If laboratory reports establish eh presence of asbestos-containing materials, these waste materials should be disposed of as asbestos-containing wastes.

BULK SAMPLING EQUIPMENT

Inspectors will need various tools and aids to accomplish their sampling tasks:
- A ladder and flashlight are needed to access areas and aid visibility
- Airtight, rigid sampling containers (e.g., 35mm film canisters)
- A plastic spray mister bottle with water to spray the area to be sampled
- Plastic drop cloths to spread beneath the area to be sampled
- A knife, linoleum cutter, cork borer, or other tool appropriate for extracting samples
- A caulking gun and compound for filling holes once a sample has been extracted
- Spray acrylic or adhesive to encapsulate sample extractions
- Duct tape or other suitable patch material for repairing thermal system insulation jackets
- Cloths (premoistened) for cleaning up debris and tools
- A vacuum cleaner equipped with high efficiency particulate air (HEPA) filters, if available; Note: non-HEPA vacuums should not be used
- Indelible ink pen for labeling sample containers
- Camera for photographic documentation
- Tape measure

ADMINISTRATIVE SUPPLIES

In addition to sampling area diagrams (see above and Section H "Inspecting for Friable and Nonfriable ACM"), data forms for bulk samples will be needed in the field. An example data form is shown in Exhibit I-5. This form is intended as a guide; you will no doubt want to tailor the form to your needs and working style. Identification labels for sample containers, packing enclosure warnings and forms, plastic bags, sturdy cartons, sealing tape, and writing materials (pens, pencils, and clipboard) are also needed.

Given the amount of equipment needed for bulk sampling, the inspector will likely need assistance. A push cart or table on wheels is worth considering to mobilize the inspection and sampling operation.

BULK SAMPLING PROCEDURES

If possible, collect samples after working hours or when the building is not in use. Steps for sampling surfacing material, thermal insulation, and miscellaneous materials are set forth below.

SURFACING MATERIALS

1. Spread the plastic drop cloth and set up other equipment, e.g., ladder.
2. Put on protective equipment (respirator at all times, protective clothing if needed).
3. Label bulk sample container with its identification number and record number, sample location, and type of material sampled on a sampling data form. Always place the label on the container itself, not on the lid, as lids can inadvertently be switched by a laboratory when handling numerous sample containers.
4. Mark the location of the sample on the sampling diagram and record the sample identification number on the plan diagram as well. Consider photographing the bulk sample collection site for project records.
5. Moisten area where sample is to be extracted (spray the immediate area with water).
6. Extract sample using a clean knife, cork borer, or other similar device to cut out or scrape off a small piece of the material. Be sure to penetrate all layers of material. Be careful not to disturb adjacent material.
7. Place sample in a container and tightly seal it.
8. Wipe the exterior of the container with a wet wipe to remove any material which may have adhered to it during sampling.
9. Clean your tools with wet wipes and wet mop or vacuum area with a HEPA vacuum to clean all debris.
10. Fill hole with caulking compound on highly friable material and/or spray with an encapsulant (to minimize subsequent fiber release) or for appearance.
11. Repeat the above steps at each sample location. Place sample containers in plastic bags.
12. Discard protective clothing, wet wipes, and rags, cartridge filters, and drop cloth in a labeled disposal bag. Seal and retain the bag until lab results are received, at which time dispose of the bag as asbestos-contaminated waste if tests were positive for asbestos. (disposal bags must be properly labeled. Disposal should be made in a state-approved landfill.) Note: Unless every sample tests negative for asbestos, discard waste as asbestos-containing material.

THERMAL SYSTEM INSULATION

Sampling thermal system insulation materials follows the same procedural sequence as laid out above. Obtain samples from exposed/damaged areas if possible. However, random sampling will require sampling of some intact material. Sampling holes can be patched with plastic spackling, caulk, or fibrous glass plus wetable fibrous glass cloth.

SAMPLE HANDLING

Care must be taken in identifying and transporting bulk samples. Specific information and sample handling procedures is provided in Section K, "Recordkeeping and Reporting."

ANALYTICAL TECHNIQUES FOR BULK SAMPLES

Polarized light microscopy (PLM) is an EPA-required method for analyzing bulk materials for asbestos. This method of analysis is relatively inexpensive. PLM utilizes a light microscope equipped with polarizing filters. The identification of asbestos fiber bundles is determined by the visual properties displayed when the sample is treated with various dispersion staining liquids. Identification is sustained by the actual structure of the fiber and the effect of polarized light on the fiber, all of which are viewed by the trained technician. The technician is also trained to give a visual estimation of the percentage of asbestos in a sample. The limit of detection of asbestos by PLM is about one percent (1%) by area. Samples containing lower levels of asbestos are not reliably detected by this technique.

Polarized Light Microscope Configuration

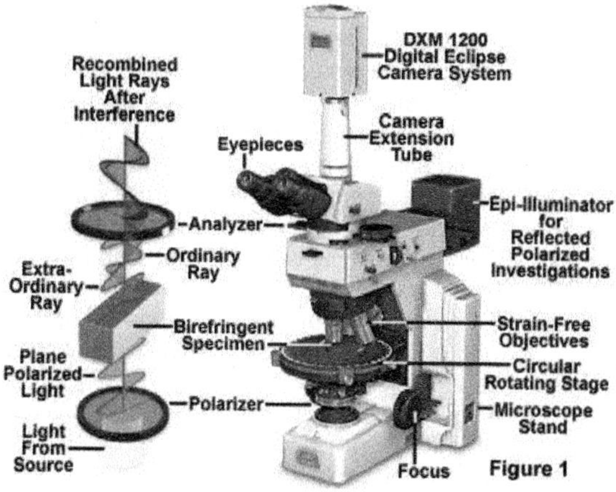

Figure 1

The U.S. EPA's NESHAP regulations require that point counting analysis be performed when analyzing samples collected from buildings or operations covered by the regulation. This technique is conducted to quantify asbestos in samples where asbestos content is less than 10% when standard PLM is used. EPA has clarified the use of point counting by stating that:

- A sample in which no asbestos is detected by polarized light microscopy does not have to be point counted provided a minimum of three slide mounts are prepared and examined to confirm no asbestos has been detected
- If the analyst detects asbestos in the sample and estimates the amount of visual estimation to be less than 10%, the owner or operator of the building may either assume the amount to be greater than 1% and treat the material as ACM, or require the verification of the amount by point counting
- If result obtained by point counting is different from a result obtained by visual estimation, the point count result must be used.

X-ray diffraction (XRD) is another method which may be used for analyzing bulk materials for asbestos. It is sometimes utilized to confirm the presence of asbestos in a sample already analyzed by PLM if the identity of the fibers remains ambiguous. XRD is not used routinely since it is not as sensitive as PLM in detecting asbestos; its limit of sensitivity is approximately three percent (3%).

Other analytical methods employed to detect the presence of asbestos in bulk samples include electron microscopy and infrared spectroscopy. Electron Microscopy may be used to detect smaller fibers of asbestos, such as those found in floor tile and fine dusts. Both techniques are sometimes used to confirm the presence of asbestos in a sample analyzed by PLM, rather than as routine analytical methods.

LABORATORY REPORTING

A competent analytical laboratory should provide a detailed bulk sample analysis report that includes the following information, at a minimum:
- Client sample identification number
- Laboratory sample identification number
- Analytical technique used
- Laboratory quality control procedures
- Physical description of sample, as received
- Type(s) and estimated percentage of asbestos
- Type(s) and estimated percentage of non-asbestos fibers
- Type(s) (if known) and percentage of other components
- Date of analysis
- Analyst's signature

Exhibit I-6 is an example laboratory reporting form.

This information, along with data generated in the field (e.g., location of sample, type of material, photo references, etc.), should be maintained as part of an overall building inspection, recordkeeping program.

QUALITY ASSURANCE

Quality assurance (QA) procedures are employed to ensure reliable results for analyses of bulk samples. The first step to assuring quality is to choose a laboratory that is competent and reliable. Laboratories should be chosen from the list of laboratories accredited through the National Voluntary Laboratory Accreditation Program (NVLAP) administered by the National Institute of Standards and Technology (NIS), in Gaithersburg, Maryland [(301) 975-4016].

The second step in a QA program is to monitor the performance of the laboratory where samples are being analyzed. EPA recommends that for every 20th bulk sample that is collected, a QA sample be taken immediately adjacent to the 20th sample. Thus the 20th and 21st samples of every group of 20 are side-by-side samples. Many building inspectors will collect a QA sample for every 10 samples collected for a greater degree of assurance. Laboratory analyses of these two samples are expected to closely agree. Each sample is labeled independently so that the identity of QA samples cannot be determined except by reference to records kept by the building inspector.

QA samples can be handled by one of two ways. They can be sent together with all the samples to a single laboratory for analysis. Alternatively, they can be sent to a second laboratory and analyzed independently. The first checks on analytical variability within the same lab. The second checks on variability between labs. Using a second laboratory is appropriate for large projects.

Laboratory results on the QA samples should not disagree on the presence or absence of asbestos (i.e., 1% or less vs. more than 1% asbestos). If significant disagreement occurs, additional samples should be taken and analyzed.

There may also be discrepancies in estimating the exact percentage of asbestos in side-by-side samples. These discrepancies are not as serious as the presence/absence result since any sample of friable material which contains more than one percent (1%) asbestos is designated as ACM. However, the comparison of the asbestos percentage estimated by the testing laboratory(ies) can provide useful information on the reliability of the analysis. Discrepancies may occur as a result of sample contamination, inconsistent procedures, differences in technique, or mistakes (e.g., mislabeling of samples). Of course, some variability in the "true" asbestos content of ACM would be expected from one location to another. Ordinarily the percentage of asbestos reported for each QA sample as compared with the percentage of asbestos reported for its corresponding regular sample should not exceed ten percent (10%).

Any disagreement about the type of asbestos mineral (chrysotile, Amosite, Crocidolite) present should be resolved by additional analyses. Information on mineral type may be important when evaluating alternative methods of managing ACM, especially if removal of the ACM is under consideration.

Procedures to assure the integrity of the samples are also a component of the QA program. Strict chain-of-custody procedures should be followed. See Section K for a description of chain-of-custody procedures and data forms.

EXHIBIT I-1

EXAMPLE SAMPLING AREA DIAGRAM

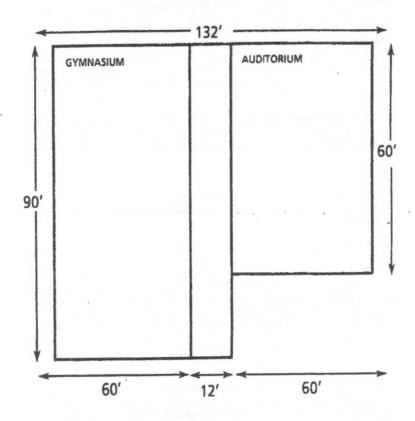

EXHIBIT I-2

EXAMPLE GRID

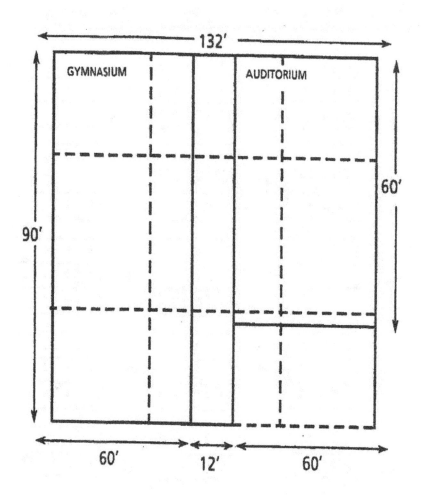

SECTION I: BULK SAMPLING OF SUSPECT MATERIALS

EXHIBIT I-3

RANDOM NUMBER DIAGRAMS

Sampling Area	Sampling Locations			Sampling Area	Sampling Locations			Sampling Area	Sampling Locations		
1	9	8	1	7	5	8	1	13	8	5	2
	2	7	6		4	3	6		3	6	9
	5	3	4		2	7	9		7	1	4
2	8	7	1	8	5	7	1	14	4	1	6
	3	9	5		6	3	4		3	9	7
	4	2	6		2	8	9		8	5	2
3	4	1	7	9	3	6	4	15	3	5	6
	2	9	6		9	2	7		9	2	8
	8	5	3		5	8	1		7	4	1
4	6	1	8	10	5	7	3	16	4	8	3
	5	9	3		8	1	6		2	5	9
	2	7	4		2	9	4		7	1	6
5	6	4	3	11	5	1	6	17	8	2	7
	1	5	8		3	4	9		4	5	3
	9	2	7		7	8	2		1	9	6
6	7	4	3	12	7	1	9	18	2	5	9
	6	1	5		2	4	5		6	1	8
	2	9	8		6	8	3		4	7	3

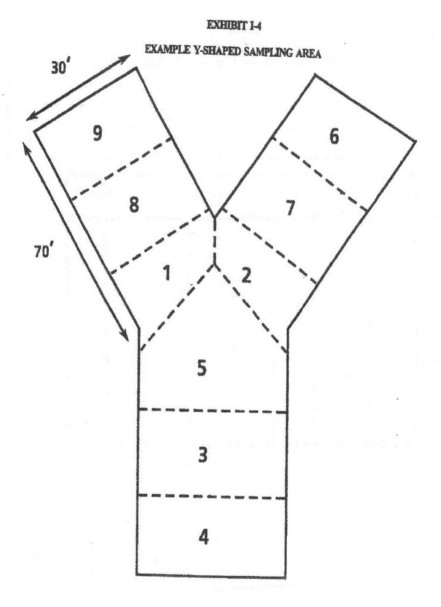

EXHIBIT I-4

EXAMPLE Y-SHAPED SAMPLING AREA

EXHIBIT I-5

EXAMPLE DATA FORM FOR BULK SAMPLES

Inspector _____

Building _____   Date_____

Sample Location				Sample No.	Type of Material	Asbestos	
Functional Space No.	Homogeneous Area No.	Floor	Room			Type	%

EXHIBIT I-6

EXAMPLE LABORATORY REPORT
ASBESTOS TEST RESULTS FORM

Sample ID#					

Analytical method
  1. PLM and dispersion staining
  2. X-ray diffraction					

Gross Sample Appearance
(enter number, note color)
  1. Homogeneous, fibrous
  2. Homogeneous, nonfibrous
  3. Heterogeneous, fibrous
  4. Heterogeneous, nonfibrous
  5. Heterogeneous, mixed					

Sample Treatment
(enter number)
  1. Homogenized
  2. Untreated
  3. Other, specify					

Total Amount of Materials Examined (mg)					

Asbestos Present
(enter number and percent)
  1. Amosite
  2. Chrysolite
  3. Crocidolite
  4. Other, specify					

Percent Total Asbestos Present in Sample					

Other Fibrous Materials Present
(enter number and percent)
  1. Fiber Glass
  2. Mineral Wool
  3. Cellulose
  4. Other, specify					

Nonfibrous Materials Present
(fill in description below by number and enter number and percent in columns)
  1.
  2.
  3.
  4.
  5.					

INTRODUCTION

Building inspectors must frequently disturb asbestos-containing materials in the course of their duties to collect bulk samples and assess the condition of the material. In most cases the Building Inspector does not know if the suspect material in fact contains asbestos. Accordingly, he or she should always assume the suspect material contains asbestos until proof is provided. As a precaution, the Building Inspector should always follow procedures for bulk sample collection which will minimize the release of fibers (i.e., wet methods, etc.). In addition, the building inspector must wear appropriate personal protective equipment for his/her own protection when performing bulk sampling and assessment activities. This will normally include a respirator and protective clothing. Depending on the specific project, additional protective measures may be necessary such as eye protection.

There are three ways that hazardous materials can enter the body: (1) through the gastrointestinal tract, usually via the mouth, (2) through the skin, and (3) through the respiratory system. Asbestos does not appear to pose a serious threat to the body through the first or second routes of entry. I can, however cause serious diseases when it enters the body through the respiratory system. (See Section B for information on health effects.)

RESPIRATORY SYSTEM

The respiratory system is a gaseous (air) pump containing a series of airways leading from the nose and mouth down into the air sacs (alveoli) where there is an exchange of oxygen and carbon dioxide. The main components of the respiratory system, from top to bottom are as follows:

- Nose and mouth
- Throat
- Larynx (voice box)
- Trachea (wind pipe)
- Bronchi (branches from the trachea)
- Alveoli (air sacs in the lung)
- Diaphragm and chest muscles

The human body has certain natural defenses to protect itself against inhaling dust. The most important of these is the muco-ciliary escalator. Airways of the upper respiratory tract (trachea through bronchi) are lined with cilia (hair-like protrusions) covered with a layer of mucous. These cilia are constantly sweeping upward quickly, then down slowly, and thus moving the mucous and trapped materials up at a rate of approximately one-inch per minute. This is an important clearance mechanism which prevents most large particles from reaching the alveoli in the lungs. Particles trapped in the mucous are carried back up to the throat where they are swallowed or expectorated. Unfortunately, this natural defense mechanism does not prevent all asbestos fibers from reaching the lungs where damage can occur. Accordingly, respirators must be worn to provide further protection when asbestos exposure is likely.

RESPIRATORY HAZARDS

Respiratory hazards are generally divided into two categories; toxic contaminants and oxygen deficiency. Generally, building inspections would not pose oxygen deficiency hazards. However, since there may be projects and circumstances where it can be a problem, oxygen deficiency must always be considered. For example, there could be an oxygen deficiency problem while inspecting in steam tunnels, mechanical chases, or boilers. Failing to consider oxygen deficiency could result in a fatality on any project.

Toxic contaminants are the more common category of respiratory hazards encountered on inspections. Those toxic contaminants are generally subdivided into two categories: particulates and gaseous materials (or a combination of the two). Asbestos fibers are an example of the particulate subcategory and carbon monoxide is an example of the gaseous subcategory. It is possible to have both of these hazardous substances, as well as others, in a work area at the same time.

The control of respiratory hazards often involved three steps:
- Assessing the hazards
- Reducing or eliminating the hazards
- Providing respiratory protective equipment

The asbestos detection and control industry is actually based on these first two steps. Buildings and other structures are inspected or surveyed to assess potential asbestos hazards. When a potential asbestos hazard exists, a group or contractor is called upon to reduce or eliminate the hazard through removal, encapsulation, or enclosure of the material. Thus, the third step, respirators, can be avoided to protect the building occupants.

RESPIRATOR CLASSIFICATIONS

There are two general categories of respiratory protection devices: air-purifying and supplied-air respirators. For most building inspections air-purifying respirators will provide the needed protection. Accordingly, the discussion of the uses and limitations of supplied-air respirators is limited. (See Exhibit J-1 for pictures of various types of respirators).

These respirators remove the hazardous contaminant from the breathing air before it is inhaled. They consist of a soft, rubber facepiece, and a replaceable filter or cartridge. Two major subcategories of air-purifying respirators are the mechanical filter type and the chemic al cartridge type. The mechanical filter variety is designed to protect against particulate contaminants such as asbestos. The chemical cartridge type protects against gaseous contaminants such as solvent vapors. Each respirator assembly is approved for a particular contaminant; care must be taken in choosing the appropriate unit. High efficiency particulate air (HEPA) filters designed for asbestos are typically purple or magenta in color. These filters will remove 99.97 percent of particles 0.3 micrometers or greater in diameter.

Air-purifying respirators are further categorized based on their degree of face coverage. The half-mask respirator covers half the face—from the bridge of the nose to under the chin. A full-face respirator covers the face from the forehead to under the chin. The more extensive coverage provides a better fit and a higher degree of protection. Air-purifying respirators depend upon breathing action to draw atmospheric air through the respirator filter or cartridge where it is decontaminated. Hence, they are referred to as "negative pressure" respirators.

POWERED AIR PURIFYING RESPIRATORS (PAPR's)

A special subcategory of air-purifying respirator is the Powered Air Purifying (PAPR) type. It uses the same types of cartridges and filters as regular air purifying respirators to clean the air. PAPRs, however, are positive pressure devices which employ a portable, rechargeable battery pack and blower to force contaminated air through a filter or cartridge, where it is cleaned and supplied to the wearer's breathing zone. PAPRs are available in both tight-fitting and loose-fitting styles. Because the air is being drawn from the immediate work area, they too offer no protection against oxygen deficiency. An advantage of using a powered air purifying respirator is that it supplies air at a positive pressure within the facepiece, helmet, or hood so that any leak is usually outward.

SUPPLIED-AIR RESPIRATOR

These respirators supply uncontaminated, breathing air from a source independent of the surrounding atmosphere. Air is delivered to the facepiece through an air-line (a hose). These respirators are often referred to as "air-line respirators". A second type of supplied air respirator is the self-contained breathing apparatus (SCBA). The user carries the source of breathable air, usually a tank of compressed air.

Airline respirators come in several distinct versions: demand, pressure-demand, and continuous-flow. They are distinguished by their regulator and valve design. EPA and NIOSH recommend the pressure-demand type if supplied-air respirators are selected.

Supplied-air respirators also have limitations
- The trailing airline restricts the user's mobility.
- The air supply of a SCBA respirator is limited.

- The bulk and weight of a SCBA respirator make it impractical for strenuous work or for use in confined spaces.
- Backup units or supplemental air-purifying respirators should be available if the air supply is interrupted.

RESPIRATORY PROTECTION PROGRAM

Respirators are commonly used to help protect against inhalation hazards. However, a respiratory protection program is not simply donning a respirator and expecting to be adequately protected.

Any employer who requires or permits employees to wear a respirator must have a written respiratory protection program. This is required by OSHA in both of their asbestos standards (29 CFR 1910.1001 and 1926.1101) and respiratory protection regulations (29 CFR 1910.134). The written respirator program established standard operating procedures concerning the use and maintenance of respiratory equipment. In addition to having such a written program, the employer must also be able to demonstrate that the program is enforced and updated as necessary.

The OSHA regulations spell out just what must be included in a written program. Below, those items are discussed with special emphasis on applications to work performed by building inspectors.

An effective respirator program as adapted from *A Guide to Respiratory Protection for the Asbestos Abatement Industry.*
1. A written statement of company policy, including assignment of individual responsibility, accountability, and authority for required activities of the respiratory protection program
2. Written standard operating procedures governing the selection and use of respirators.
3. Respirator selection (from NIOSH/MSHA approved and certified models) on the basis of hazards to which the worker is exposed.
4. Medical examination of workers to determine whether or not they may be assigned an activity where respiratory protection is required.
5. User training in the proper use and limitations of respirators (as well as a way to evaluate the skill and knowledge obtained by the worker through training).
6. Respirator fit testing
7. Regular cleaning and disinfecting of respirators
8. Routine inspection of respirators during cleaning, and at least once a month and after each use for those respirators designated for emergency use.
9. Storage of respirators in convenient, clean, and sanitary locations.
10. Surveillance of work area conditions and degree of employee exposure (e.g., through air monitoring).

11. Regular inspection and evaluation of the continued effectiveness of the program

All of the above items are required by OSHA if employees wear negative pressure respirators during work or if the OSHA permissible exposure limit (PEL) or excursion limit (EL) is exceeded (See Section L for more information on OSHA requirements). Although not required, one additional program element is recommended:

12. Recognition and resolution of special problems as they affect respirator use (e.g., facial hair, eye glasses, etc.)

ESTABLISHING A POLICY

Every employer should prepare a clear concise policy regarding the use of respirators by their employees when performing building inspection activities for asbestos. This policy should serve as the guiding principal for the preparation, implementation, and enforcement of an effective respiratory protection program.

DESIGNATION OF A PROGRAM ADMINISTRATOR

A program administrator must be designated by name. This person is responsible for implementation of, and adherence to, the provisions of the respiratory protection program. It is usually a good idea to also designate a person who is responsible for enforcement of the procedures at each job site. This may apply to a building inspector or management planner individually. Procedures should also be outlined for enforcement of the program. Enforcement procedures and the development of the program as a whole should be done in conjunction with and input from the employees and/or their representative(s).

SELECTION AND USE OF RESPIRATORY PROTECTION EQUIPMENT

The selection of appropriate respiratory equipment generally involves three steps:

1. Identifying the hazards
2. Evaluating the hazards
3. Providing proper respiratory protection equipment to suit the conditions and the individual.

The purpose of inspecting buildings and structures is to determine the presence (or absence) of ACM and to identify conditions which are potentially hazardous. Until the level of hazard is evaluated, building inspectors should assume that fiber levels could be high enough to be of concern.

The respirator selected and the respiratory program established must conform to Occupational Safety and Health Administration (OSHA) standards, and guidelines published by respirator manufacturers. The OSHA respirator standard (29 CFR 1910.134) requires that only approved respirators be used. In addition, the respirator must be approved for protection specifically against asbestos fibers.

The National Institute for Occupational Safety and Health (NIOSH) is the official respirator testing and approval agency for respirators. If the entire respirator assembly including cartridges, filters, and hoses, passes NIOSH test criteria, then NIOSH issues an approval number. The specific number is preceded by the letters "TC", which indicates the respirator assembly was "Tested and Certified".

In addition to any assigned identification number associated with each unit, the NIOSH approved respirator is accompanied by a label identifying the type of hazard the respirator is designed to protect against; additional information on the label which indicates limitations and identifies the component parts approved for use with the basic unit.

Although some single-use disposable dust masks were at one time "approved" by NIOSH for use with asbestos, they should not be used during asbestos inspections. NIOSH has stated that these respirators do not provide adequate protection against asbestos. As a rule of thumb, negative pressure, air-purifying respirators with HEPA filters may be used during building inspections.

PROTECTION FACTORS

Respirators offer varying degrees of protection against asbestos fibers. The key to understanding the differences between types of respirators (air-purifying, powered-air purifying, air-supplied) is the amount of protection afforded the wearer. To compare these, one must understand the concept of a protection factor (PF).

A protection factor is a number obtained when the concentration of a contaminant outside the mask is divided by the concentration found inside the mask. This simple formula is illustrated below.

$$\text{Protection Factor (PF)} = \frac{\text{Conc. Outside mask}}{\text{Conc. Inside mask}}$$

The protection factor depends greatly on the fit of the mask to the wearer's face. Accordingly, the protection offered by any one respirator will be different for each individual person. Further, the protection constantly changes depending upon the worker's activities and even shaving habits. When a worker laughs or coughs inside a respirator, the protection factor will decrease since the mask will not "fit" as well during laughing and coughing. Similarly, a worker who forgot to shave one morning will not receive as much protection that day since the mask will not fit as well to the face. The importance of properly fitting the mask should now be obvious.

It is virtually impossible to measure the concentration inside the mask (where the worker is breathing) for each worker, all the time, during various activities he or she may be conducting. Accordingly, protection factors, based on extensive research, have been developed for different categories of respirators. Using these protection factors, it is easy to determine what type of respirator is appropriate to maintain the concentration of asbestos inside the mask below a certain level. (A level of 0.01 fibers per cubic centimeter (f/cc) is often cited as the desired level inside the mask.) Using established protection factors, the inspector may select from Table J-1 the appropriate respirator to maintain the concentration inside the respirator below 0.01 f/cc. It should be noted that the protection factors for powered-air purifying respirators are estimated on the most recent data available. (Supplied-air respirators are not included since they are unlikely to be needed by building inspectors.)

TABLE J-1
SUGGESTED RESPIRATOR SELECTION FOR PROTECTION AGAINST ASBESTOS WHEN PROPERLY FITTED FOR USE AND PROPERLY MAINTAINED

(per OSHA not NIOSH)

Respirator Selection	PF	Maximum airborne fiber concentration outside the respirator to maintain exposure inside the respirator below 0.01 fibers/cc
High efficiency air-purifying type (half mask)	10	0.10 fibers/cc
High efficiency air-purifying type (full face mask)	50	0.50 fibers/cc
Powered air-purifying helmet type (PAPR)	25	0.25 fibers/cc
Powered air-purifying (PAPR) tight fitting mask	1,000	0.10 fibers/cc

MEDICAL SURVEILLANCE

Only those individuals who are medially capable to wear respiratory protection equipment shall be issued one. Before being issued a respirator, an employee will receive pertinent tests for medial and physical conditions. Medical tests to be conducted by a physician often include: pulmonary function tests, a chest x-ray (if a physical deems it necessary), electrocardiogram, and any other tests deemed appropriate by the examining physician. A medical history in the form of a questionnaire is collected as well for each individual. Other factors to be considered by a physician may include: emphysema, asthma, chronic bronchitis, heart disease, anemia, hemophilia, poor eyesight, poor hearing, hernia, lack of use of fingers or hands, epileptic seizures, and other factors which might inhibit the ability of an employee to wear respiratory equipment.

EMPLOYEE TRAINING PROGRAM

Each employee designated to wear a respirator must receive adequate training. The training session (initial and periodic training) should be conducted by a qualified individual to ensure that employees understand the limitations, use, and maintenance of respiratory equipment. The OSHA Asbestos Standards require that employee training be repeated at least annually.

RESPIRATOR FITTING

One of the most important elements of an effective respirator program is fitting. The OSHA Asbestos Standards (29 CFR 1910.1001 and 1926.1101) and the OSHA Respirator Standard (29 CFR 1910.134) require that the fit of respirators be tested when the respirator is issued, and every six months thereafter for all negative pressure respirators. The fit of the respirator should also be checked each time it is worn. Procedures for fit-testing and fit-checking should be addressed in the written respirator program.

Once the appropriate respirator has been selected for the contaminant and conditions to which an individual is exposed, the respirator must be fit-tested. A respirator will not provide protection unless the air passes through the filter or canister, or unless all of the air comes from the supply system. If the face seal is not tight or the connections are loos, an individual may think he or she is breathing through the purifying system, but may actually be breathing around it.

Several different respirators may have to be tried before one is found that fits properly. For any face fitting type respirator, beards and bushy sideburns may have to be shaved. Respirator facepieces generally will not seal over them. Similarly, gum and tobacco chewing cannot be permitted since excess facial movement can break the faceseal. If a person wears prescription glasses, a respirator facepiece which will accommodate the glasses should be considered. Contact lenses should not be worn while wearing a respirator.

There are two types of fit-checks, positive- and negative-pressure, and there are two categories of fit-testing, qualitative (pass/fail) and quantitative (measures levels within the mask). Only those tests applicable to asbestos work are discussed below.

Negative Pressure Fit Check

For this test, the wearer closes off the inlet of the filters or cartridges by covering them with the palms of the hands or by squeezing the breathing tube so that air cannot pass through, inhales so that the facepiece collapses slightly, and holds his/her breath for about 10 seconds. If the facepiece remains slightly collapsed and no inward leakage of air is detected, the respirator passes the test. This test can only be used on respirators with tight fitting facepieces. Its potential drawback is that hand pressure can modify the facepiece seal and cause false returns.

Positive Pressure Fit Check

This test is similar in principle to the negative pressure test. It is conducted by closing off the exhalation valve of the respirator and gently exhaling into the facepiece. The respirator fit is considered passing if positive pressure can be built up inside the facepiece without evidence of outward air leakage around the facepiece. Remember, these two fit-checks should also be done every time a respirator is put on.

If the respirator selected fails to pass these simple tests, the fit-testing should not proceed further. Instead, another size or another brand should be donned and these tests repeated. Alternatively, it may be necessary to adjust the straps on the respirator and repeat the tests. Once the wearer has successfully passed the negative and positive pressure fit-checks, the actual fit-test may be conducted. The OSHA standards permit qualitative fit-testing for half-mask-air-purifying respirators. Quantitative fit-testing is required for full-face air-purifying respirators.

QUALITATIVE FIT TESTING

During fit testing, the respirator straps must be properly located, in accordance with the manufacturer's direction, and must be as comfortable as possible. Over-tightening the straps will sometimes reduce facepiece leakage, but the wearer may be unable to tolerate the respirator for any length of time. The facepiece should not press into the face and shut off blood circulation or cause major discomfort. At the time of respirator selection, a visual inspection of the fit should always be made by a second person.

Once the respirator has been selected, and no visual leaks are evident, a negative pressure check and a positive pressure check are performed by the wearer. The simple procedures are described above.

The actual qualitative fit-test method chosen is at the discretion of the employer as long as it is one of the three specified in Appendix C of the OSHA Asbestos Standards (29 CFR 1910.1001 or 29 CFR 1926.1101). The procedures used must follow those in this appendix whether irritant smoke, isoamyl acetate, or saccharin is chosen as the test agent. The irritant smoke test is summarized below.

Irritant smoke test

If the positive and negative pressure fit checks were successful, the irritant smoke test is administered. It can be used for both air-purifying and supplied air respirators. However, an air-purifying respirator must have high efficiency filters. The test substance is an irritant smoke (stannic chloride or titanium tetrachloride). Sealed glass and plastic tubes with substances to generate this smoke are available from safety supply companies. When the tube ends are broken and air passed through them with a squeeze bulb, a dense, irritating smoke is emitted.

For the test, the respirator wearer enters a test enclosure, a clear suspended plastic bag is sufficient, and the irritant smoke is sprayed/squeezed into a small hole punched in the bag near the respirator wearers head. If the wearer detects the irritant smoke inside the respirator, it indicates a defective fit; the respirator fails this test. The advantage to this test is that the wearer usually reacts involuntarily to leakage by coughing or sneezing. The likelihood of pretending to pass this test is low.

Note: This test must be performed with caution because the irritant smoke is highly irritating to the eyes, skin, and mucous membranes. When testing a half-face mask respirator, the yes must be kept tightly closed.

QUANTITATIVE FIT-TESTING

Quantitative fit-testing requires a detectible test substance which can be generated into the air, specialized equipment to measure the airborne concentration of the substance, and a trained tester. A sodium chloride solution or corn oil is usually used to perform these tests. The person to be tested puts on a probed version of the respirator and enters a chamber which contains the test substance in the air. The airborne concentration of the substance is measure outside the respirator and inside the respirator while the tester mimics several typical work related activities. The specific degree of protection-fit factor-can be determined for the wearer and respirator.

In the past, quantitative fit testing was usually performed in a laboratory. However, portable fit testing units are available and some companies offer on-site testing.

CLEANING AND DISINFECTION OF RESPIRATORS

Whenever possible, a respirator should be reserved for the exclusive use of a single individual. Following each use, the respirators should be cleaned and disinfected. The following procedures can be used to clean with a respirator:
- Wash with a detergent or a combination detergent and disinfectant, in warm water using a brush
- Rinse in clean water, or rinse once with a disinfectant and once with clean water. The clean water rinse is particularly important because traces of detergent or disinfectant left on the mask can cause skin irritation and/or damage respirator components.

- Air dry on a rack or hang; position the respirator so that the facepiece elastomer will not be deformed during drying.

ROUTINE INSPECTIONS OF RESPIRATORS

Inspection of the respirator is an important, routine task. It should be done before and after each use. The respirator should be checked for the following defects:

A.   Air-purifying respirators (half-mask and full facepiece)

Elastomeric facepiece should be checked for
   a.   Excessive dirt
   b.   Cracks, tears, or holes
   c.   Distortion from improper storage
   d.   Cracked, scratched, or loose fitting lens
   e.   Broken or missing mounting clips

Headstraps should be checked for
   a.   Breaks or tears
   b.   Loss of elasticity
   c.   Broken or malfunctioning buckles or attachments
   d.   Excessively worn serrations of the head harness which might allow the facepiece to slip

Inhalation valve, exhalation valve, should be checked for:
   a.   Detergent residue, dust particles, or dirt on valve seat
   b.   Cracks, tears, or distortion in the valve material or valve seat
   c.   Missing or defective valve cover

Filter elements should be checked for:
   a.   Proper filter for the hazard
   b.   Approval designation (TC #)
   c.   Missing or worn gaskets
   d.   Worn threads
   e.   Cracks or dents in filter housing

B.   Powered Air Purifying Respirators

Check facepiece, headstraps, valve, and breathing tube, as for regular air purifying respirators.

Hood or helmet, if applicable, checks for:
   a.   Headgear suspension (adjust properly for wearer)
   b.   Cracks or breaks in faceshield (replace faceshield)

C.   Supplied Air Respirators

Facepiece, headstrap, and valves should be checked as specified above. In addition the following checks should be performed:

Breathing tube should be checked for:
    a.   Cracks
    b.   Missing or loose hose clamps
    c.   Broken or missing connectors

Hood, helmet, or suit should be checked for:
    a.   Headgear suspension
    b.   Cracks or breaks in faceshield
    c.   Rips and torn seams

Air supply system should be checked for
    a.   Breaks or kinks in air supply hoses and end fitting attachments
    b.   Tightness of connections
    c.   Proper setting of regulators and valves (consult manufacturer's recommendations)
    d.   Correct operation of air purifying elements and carbon monoxide or high-temperature alarms

REPAIR

At some point any respirator will need replacement parts or some other repair. OSHA requires that the person who repairs respirators be trained and qualified. It is important to realize that respirator parts from different manufacturers are not interchangeable. NIOSH approval is invalidated if parts are substituted.

RESPIRATOR STORAGE

Proper storage is very important. OSHA requires that respirators be protected from dust, sunlight, heat, extreme cold, excessive moisture, and damaging or contaminating chemicals. When not in use, the respirator should be placed in a closed plastic bag, and stored in a clean, convenient, sanitary location.

SURVEILLANCE OF WORKING CONDITIONS

An employer must provide adequate surveillance of the employee's working conditions to be certain the respirator provides adequate protection. In the case of building inspectors this includes a determination if other hazardous airborne contaminants might be encountered for which the respirator chosen is not adequate. It may also include periodic air monitoring to estimate the asbestos exposure. This provides the needed information to determine if the respirator chosen affords sufficient protection to the individual.

RESPIRATOR PROGRAM EVALUATION AND RECORDKEEPING

The respirator program shall be evaluated a least annually with program adjustments, as appropriate, made to reflect air sampling or other evaluation results. Compliance with the aforementioned points of the program should be reviewed; respirator selection, purchase of approved equipment, medical screening of employees, fit testing, issuance of equipment and appropriate maintenance, storage, repair and inspection, appropriate surveillance of work area conditions.

Attention should be given to proper recordkeeping. Records which should be kept include: names of employees trained in respirator use, documentation of the care and maintenance of respirators, medical reports of each respirator user, possible airborne concentrations of asbestos fibers during work, and any problems encountered during projects with regards to respiratory equipment. A checklist for self-evaluation of a respiratory protection program is included as Exhibit J-2.

PROTECTIVE CLOTHING

It is important to understand why protective clothing may need to be worn during building inspections. The primary reason is to keep gross amounts of suspected asbestos-containing debris off of the body, hair, etc. The use of protective clothing will minimize the chance of brining asbestos out of a facility and into the home. Protective clothing may become necessary when inspecting heavily contaminated crawl spaces, mechanical rooms, etc., or when material is significantly damaged in certain locations such that it could cause an inspector's street clothes to become contaminated. Protective clothing for inspection purposes may consist of disposable body coveralls, foot covering, and head covering. The foot and head covering should be attached to the coveralls. This eliminates the need to tape openings between garments. For inspection purposes, protective clothing may be worn over the inspector's street clothes. The disposable coveralls, foot, and head coverings are available from many sources and constructed of several materials. Coveralls, with foot and head covering attached usually cost about $2.50 each when purchased in quantity. Separately, the coveralls cost approximately $2.00, head covering about $0.35, and foot covering about $0.50 per pair. It is important to realize that many "bargain" prices may not be a bargain at all. The less expensive coveralls often use less material. Accordingly, coveralls marked "XL" may be too small for many inspectors. Be sure to check the construction of the coveralls as well. Double stitching on seams will last longer, but cost more. When leaving an inspection site, the inspector should exercise care in removing protective clothing.

1. HEPA vacuum off any debris accumulated on the inspectors garments.
2. Remove all protective garments and equipment (except respirator) in an isolated area.

3.   All disposable clothing should be placed in plastic bags and labeled as asbestos-containing waste.

4.   Non-disposable clothing should be sealed in a plastic bag and labeled as asbestos-contaminated clothing. Procedures for handling and laundering of asbestos-contaminated clothing must be in compliance with the OSHA asbestos standard 29 CFR 1926.1101.

5.   Once the plastic bag is properly sealed, respirators may be removed.

OTHER PERSONAL PROTECTIVE EQUIPMENT

Additional protective equipment may be necessary depending on the specific project. The most common other protective equipment will include eye protection. This is especially important when collecting bulk samples from suspect materials located overhead. Goggles or safety glasses (with side shields) are often adequate. Hard hats, safety shoes, and hearing protection may also be necessary on certain projects.

EXHIBIT J-2 RESPIRATOR PROGRAM CHECKLIST

In general, the respirator program should be evaluated at least annually with program adjustments, as appropriate, made to reflect the evaluation results. Program function can be separated into administration and operations.

1.   Program Administration

_____   (1) Is there is a written policy which acknowledges employer responsibility for providing a safe and healthful workplace, and assigns program responsibility, accountability, and authority?

_____   (2) Is program responsibility vested in one individual who is knowledgeable and who can coordinate all aspects of the program at the job site?

_____   (3) Can feasible engineering controls or work practices eliminate the need for respirators?

_____   (4) Are there written procedures/statements covering the various aspects of the respirator program, including:

_____designation of an administrator

_____respirator selection

_____purchase of approved equipment

_____medical aspects of respirator usage

_____issuance of equipment

_____fitting

_____training

_____maintenance, storage, and repair

_____inspection

_____use under special conditions

_____work area under surveillance

2.   Program Operation

(1) Respiratory protective equipment selection and assignment

_____ Are work area conditions and employee exposures properly surveyed?

_____ Are respirators selected on the basis of hazards which the employee is selected?

_____ Are selections made by individuals knowledgeable of proper selection Procedures?

_____ Are only approved respirators purchased and used; do they provide adequate protection for the specific hazard and concentration of the contaminant?

_____ Has a medical evaluation of the prospective user been made to determine physical and psychological ability to wear the selected respiratory protective equipment?

_____ Where practical, have respirators been issued to the users for their exclusive use, and are there records covering issuance?

(2) Respiratory protective equipment fitting

_____ Are the users given the opportunity to try on several respirators to determine whether the respirator they will subsequently be wearing is the best fitting one?

_____ Is the fit tested at appropriate intervals?

_____ Are those users who require corrective lenses properly fitted?

_____ Are users prohibited from wearing contact lenses when using respirators?

_____ Is the facepiece-to-face seal tested in a test atmosphere?

_____ Are workers prohibited from entering contaminated work areas when they have facial hair or other characteristics which prohibit the use of tight-fitting facepieces?

(3) Respirator use

_____ Are respirators being worn correctly (i.e., head covering over respirator straps)?

_____ Are workers keeping respirators on all the time when necessary?

(4) Maintenance of respiratory protective equipment

(a) Cleaning and disinfecting

_____ Are respirators cleaned and disinfected after each use?

_____ Are proper methods of cleaning and disinfecting utilized?

(b) Storage

_____ Are respirators stored in a manner so as to protect them from dust, sunlight, heat, excessive cold or moisture, or damaging chemicals?

_____ Are respirators stored properly in storage facility so as to prevent them from deforming?

_____ Is storage in lockers and tool boxes permitted only if the respirator is in a carrying case or carton?

(c) Inspection

_____ Are respirators inspected before and after each use and during cleaning?

_____ Are qualified individuals/users instructed in inspection techniques?

_____ Is respiratory protective equipment designated as "emergency use" inspected at least monthly? (in addition to after each use)

_____ Is a record kept of the inspection of "emergency use" respiratory protective equipment?

(d) Repair

_____ Are replacement parts used in repair, those of the manufacturer of the respirator?

(5) Special Use Conditions

_____ Is a procedure developed for respiratory protective equipment usage in atmospheres immediately dangerous to life or health?

_____ Is a procedure developed for equipment usage for entry into confined spaces?

(6) Training

_____ Are users trained in proper respirator use, cleaning, and inspection?

_____ Are users trained in the basis for selection of respirators?

_____ Are users evaluated, using competency-based evaluation, before and after training?

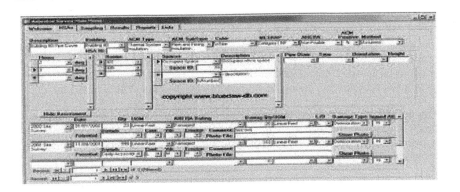

OBJECTIVES:

1. To develop an appropriate bulk sample labeling scheme
2. To employ appropriate handling and recordkeeping procedures for bulk samples.
3. To become knowledgeable of the reporting requirements as outlined in AHERA.

PROCEDURES FOR SAMPLE LABELING AND SHIPPING

To ensure that the samples collected are neither lost nor their identity confused, the handling of all samples from point of collection to receipt at a testing laboratory requires adherence to procedures and detail. The procedures outlined below and the accompanying data forms are intended as an illustrative model. The purpose of the sampling protocol is threefold: to protect the samples form damage, to reduce the possibility of misidentifying individual; samples, and to provide a means for tracing any samples that may be lost.

PRIOR TO SAMPLE COLLECTION

Determine a scheme for assigning sampled identification numbers. For example, starting with 1000, label each sample consecutively through 1010. The next sample you take is a Quality Assurance (QA) sample, number 2010. Resume consecutive numbering with 1011 and continue through 1020, at this point you will take another QA sample, number 2020. This scheme allows you to quickly distinguish regular and QA samples.

AT THE POINT OF SAMPLE COLLECTION

After placing in a container according to the procedures outlined earlier, affix a sample identification sticker on the container. Peelable, self-stick labels are available in various sizes and work well for this purpose. Enter the identification number on the <u>Chain of Custody Sheet</u>; Exhibit K-1 is a sample Chain of Custody Sheet. On the building floor plan map, mark the location from which the sample was drawn, and record the sample identification number. Place the sample containers in a plastic bag. Where possible, and especially in maintenance areas, directly mark the sample location with the sample number. This may not be feasible with flooring materials, but works very well with TSI in particular.

If an independent laboratory is to be employed to analyze QA samples, separate Chain of Custody Sheets for each laboratory will be needed-one to accompany regular samples, one for QA samples. Place all regularly and all QA samples in separate plastic bags.

UPON THE CONCLUSION OF SAMPLING

Remove the containers holding the samples from the plastic bag, checking to see that the cover and label are securely fastened. Place them in a shipping box with appropriate packing material (bubble pack, or other stuffing material). Duplicate the completed Chain of Custody Sheet(s) and place the original in the shipping box, retaining a copy for your records. Place the warning label in the box and securely seal the box. Completion of a laboratory generated data sheet may be required by the lab. Ship or hand delivers regular samples and QA samples to the appropriate testing or QA laboratory. Exhibit K-2 shows the procedures for handling samples.

AT THE LABORATORY

Upon receipt of samples from the building inspector, the laboratory should check and sign the chain of custody sheets, copy them, and return the original(s) to the inspector. It is important that this or a similar arrangement for sample accountability be agreed upon by the laboratory prior to sending samples for analysis.

Samples will be analyzed for asbestos using one of the techniques described in Section I. Results of these tests will be sent to the inspector. You may opt to have the laboratory retain and store the samples, usually for a fee, or return them to you for future disposition.

REPORTING

LABORATORY REPORT

Accredited laboratories will provide clients with a written report containing the results of their analyses. The report must contain the following information:
- The name and address of the laboratory

- The date of the analysis
- The name and signature of the person performing the analyses
- The results of the analyses

The building inspector is responsible for submitting this information to the designated person responsible for implementing the AHERA requirements at a school, or the Asbestos Program Manager for a building or facility employing his/her services.

INSPECTION REPORT

Within 30 days of conducting a school building inspection, a full written report is to be submitted to the school district or the district's designated representative. AHERA prescribes that the following information be included in the report.

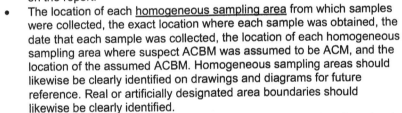

- The date(s) of the inspection
- The name and signature of each accredited person conducting the inspection, collecting samples, and making the assessment. The State of accreditation and, if applicable, the accreditation number of each inspector is to be provided on the report.
- The location of each <u>homogeneous sampling area</u> from which samples were collected, the exact location where each sample was obtained, the date that each sample was collected, the location of each homogeneous sampling area where suspect ACBM was assumed to be ACM, and the location of the assumed ACBM. Homogeneous sampling areas should likewise be clearly identified on drawings and diagrams for future reference. Real or artificially designated area boundaries should likewise be clearly identified.
- A discussion of the manner used to determine sampling locations. Logic used in choosing sample locations should be presented and defended in writing. Sample locations should be selected for their ability to be representative of selected areas. To enable the samples to be statistically random, a protocol like that provided in the EPA guidance publication "Simplified Sampling Scheme for Friable Surfacing Materials"
- A list of identified homogeneous sampling areas and their classification as to type of material. All areas are to be identified by material types as either surfacing material, thermal system insulation, or miscellaneous material
- Following receipt of the results of laboratory analyses, each sample and each homogeneous sampling area should be designated as ACM or non-ACM on building records.

- The assessment of the ACBM and suspected ACBM into one of the following categories:
  - Damaged or significantly damaged thermal system insulation ACM.
  - Damaged friable surfacing ACM
  - Significantly damaged friable surfacing ACM
  - Damaged or significantly damaged friable miscellaneous ACM
  - ACBM with potential for damage
  - ACBM with potential for significant damage
  - Any remaining friable ACBM or friable suspected ACBM

The contents of the building inspector's report will be incorporated into the Management Plan to be developed in the next phase of compliance with AHERA.

EXHIBIT K-1

EXAMPLE CHAIN-OF-CUSTODY FORM

Building _____

Sample I.D.	Condition Shipped	Condition received	Condition Analyzed

Signature of Sender _____

Signature of Receiver _____

Signature of Analyst _____

EXHIBIT K-2

SAMPLE HANDLING PROCEDURES

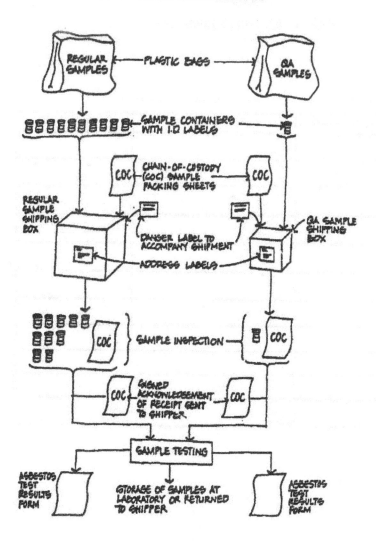

SECTION L: REGULATORY REVIEW

INTRODUCTION

Two federal agencies have been principally responsible for generating regulations for asbestos control. These two agencies are the U.S. Environmental Protection Agency (EPA) and the U.S. Occupational Safety and Health Administration (OSHA).

Other federal agencies with jurisdiction over asbestos detection and control include the Department of Transportation (DOT) whose regulations govern the transport of asbestos, the National Institute of Standards and Technology (NIST) which establishes standards and protocols for laboratory accreditation, and the Consumer Product Safety Commission (CPSC) which is responsible for banning asbestos in some products. Exhibit L-1 presents a chronology of major federal initiatives regarding asbestos. These initiatives span the period of the early 1970s through the present.

A summary of EPA and OSHA regulation follows. Specifically, the EPA Asbestos Hazard Emergency Response Act (AHERA), the EPA Asbestos School Hazard Abatement Reauthorization Act (ASHARA), the EPA National Emission Standards for Hazardous Air Pollutants (NESHAP), the EPA Asbestos Ban and Phase-Out Rule, the EPA Worker Protection Rule, and the OSHA Asbestos Standards are covered.

ASBESTOS REGULATIONS

ASBESTOS HAZARD EMERGENCY RESPONSE ACT (AHERA)

In October 1986, the Asbestos Hazard Emergency Response Act (AHERA) was signed into law. Included in this Act are provisions directing the EPA to establish rules and regulations addressing asbestos-containing materials in schools. Specifically, EPA was directed to address the issues of: (1) identifying, (2) evaluating, and (3) controlling ACM in schools.

The final AHERA regulations (rules) became effective December 14, 1987. They are found in 40 CFR 763 Subpart E §763.80-§763.99 and have authority under the Toxic Substances Control Act (TSCA).

To whom do the AHERA Regulations apply?
- All public and private elementary and secondary schools in the U.S. and its territories; and
- American schools on military bases in foreign countries.

What are the schools' responsibilities under the rule [§763.80 and .84]

149

- To designate a person to ensure that AHERA requirements are properly implemented;
- To inspect and identify friable and non-friable ACBM;
- To assess the condition of all friable known or assumed ACBM and all thermal system insulation
- To monitor and periodically reinspect;
- To develop and update management plans;
- To determine and implement response actions;
- To develop and implement operations and maintenance programs;
- To notify parents, building occupants, and outside contractors of ACM identified in the building; and
- To ensure that accredited persons perform these required activities under AHERA.

What was the timeframe for conducting building inspections under AHERA?
- Schools had to be inspected prior to October 12, 1988 [§763.85]
- After October 12, 1988 a building has to be inspected prior to its use as a school.
- Reinspections must be conducted by accredited inspectors at least once every 3 years with periodic surveillance conducted by maintenance/custodial staff every 6 months. [§763.85 and .92]

What requirements regarding bulk sampling are specified in AHERA? [§763.86]
- Schools could have elected to assume that any or all suspect materials contained asbestos. If they choose to make this assumption, sampling was necessary.
- To determine whether suspect material contains asbestos, bulk sampling must be conducted in the manner specified.

Where and how are bulk samples to be analyzed?
- Bulk samples are to be analyzed for asbestos by laboratories accredited by the National Institute of Standards and Technology (NIST) through the National Voluntary Laboratory Accreditation Program (NVLAP). [§763.87]
- Analysis shall be polarized light microscopy (PLM), using the prescribed method. (see guidance form EPA addressing point counting of bulk samples at the end of this section—Exhibit L-2).

What assessment data must be compiled by the schools? [§763.88]
- All friable ACBM thermal system insulation (TSI) and friable assumed ACBM must be located and categorized as to present conditions, potential for damage, and type of material.
- Non-friable ACBM and assumed ACM must be identified and documents but not assessed.

What options does the school have to manage and control ACM?

CAUTION
ASBESTOS
HAZARDOUS
DO NOT DISTURB WITHOUT
PROPER TRAINING AND EQUIPMENT

- Consideration may be given to the following response actions [§763.90]
  - Encapsulation;
  - Enclosure
  - Operations and maintenance
  - Repair; and
  - Removal
- Particular conditions require specific response actions.

When must a school implement an operations and maintenance (O&M) program? [§763.91]
- Any building where friable ACBM is present or assumed to be present must develop and implement an O&M program. Nonfriable ACBM is regulated under this program when it is about to be made friable due to maintenance work
- OSHA Construction Standards [29 CFR 763.1101] and/or EPA's worker Protection Rule [40 CFR 763.121] covers workers performing O&M and report activities
- The O&M program must provide for surveillance of ACM a least every six months. Additional requirements and directions for responding to fiber release episodes are specified in the regulations

What does AHERA require of schools to substantiate that they are taking responsible action to manage and control asbestos in school buildings? [§763.93]
- On or before October 12, 1988, schools must have prepared and submitted to an Agency designated by the Governor, and an asbestos management plan for each school building. The plan must be kept up-to-date
- The plan is required to contain information specified in AHERA
- Schools must have begun implementation of the management plan by July 9, 1989
- A management plan must have been prepared and submitted for any building to come into service after October 12, 1988 prior to its use as a school

What recordkeeping responsibilities does the LEA have? [§763.94]
- A detailed written description of any preventative or response action taken for ACBM must be appended to the management plan.
- Records of air monitoring, training, surveillance, cleaning, O&M, fiber release episodes, and reinspections must be maintained and added to the management plan.

Does the school have to warn persons of the presence of ACBM? [§763.95]

- Warnings must be posted adjacent to any ACBM located in maintenance areas of a building.

Are there are penalties for not complying with AHERA? [§763.97]

- Failure to comply can result in fines ranging from $5,000 to $25,000 per day in violation.
- Criminal penalties can be invoked.

Can a LEA be excluded from any part of this rule? [§763.99]

- An inspection is not necessary if an accredited inspector determines:
- that a previous inspection identified friable and non-friable ACBM (however, while sampling is not necessary in this case, the friable ACBM must be assessed as under §763.88 and the non-friable ACBM must be assessed to determine whether it has become friable);
- that prior sampling showing no ACBM was conducted in substantial compliance with AHERA;
- that all ACM was removed; or
- that the school was built after October 12, 1988 and a registered architect, project engineer or accredited inspector verifies that no ACBM was used as a building material in the building.

Who must be accredited under AHERA?

- Building Inspectors - persons who survey buildings for the presence of ACM.
- Management Planners - persons who conduct hazard assessments and who advise school administrators on management options.
- Project Designers - persons who design abatement projects and write contract specifications for abatement work.
- Abatement Supervisors - persons who supervise abatement projects.
- Abatement Workers - persons who conduct abatement projects.

Who else needs training under AHERA?

- O & M Workers - persons involved in operations and maintenance or custodial activities within a school containing ACBM
- Designated Person - person designated to ensure that the LEA responsibilities are properly implemented.

How much training is needed and how often?

- Building Inspector: 3-day course with mock building inspection and exam, half day annual refresher training.
- Management Planner: 3-day building inspectors course plus 2 additional days and exam, 1 day annual refresher training.

- Project Designer-3 day course with workshops, field trip, and exam, or abatement supervisor course, 1 day annual project designer refresher training
- Abatement Supervisor-5 day course with hands-on training and exam, 1 day annual refresher training.
- Abatement Worker-4 day course with hand-on training and exam, 1 day annual refresher training.
- O & M Workers*-2 hour awareness for any maintenance or custodial workers who work in a building which contains asbestos; 14 additional hours for any maintenance or custodial workers who may disturb ACBM through their work.
- Designated Person*-training adequate to perform duties as required under 763.84

What responsibilities does a state have under AHERA?
- Each is to adopt an accreditation plan at least as stringent as the EPA model.
- An agency of the state was to be named to receive and review LEA's Management Plan.

ASBESTOS SCHOOL HAZARD ABATEMENT REAUTHORIZATION ACT (ASHARA)

Section 206 of the Toxic Substance Control Act (TSCA) mandated that EPA develop and asbestos Model Accreditation Plan (MAP). The original MAP was promulgated in 1987 and became codified as 40 CFR Part 763; Appendix C to Subpart E. Section 206 of TSCA was later amended by the Asbestos School Hazard Abatement Reauthorization Act (ASHARA). ASHARA mandated that the MAP be revised to:
- Provide for the extension of accreditation requirements to public and commercial buildings for persons who inspect for asbestos-containing material, design response actions, or carry out response actions; and
- Increase the minimum number of training hours, including additional hands-on training, required for accreditation of workers and supervisors performing work in schools and/or public and commercial buildings.

ASHARA does not require persons who prepare management plans in public or commercial buildings to obtain accreditation. The accreditation requirements of the ASHARA statue went into effect on November 28, 1992. The revised MAP, which provides more information on the meaning of the new statutory requirements, and expands the length of, and/or topics addressed in the training courses, were published as an interim final rule in the *Federal Register* on February 3, 1994, and took effect on April 4, 1994.

As part of the ASHARA regulations, EPA has defined an inspection to be an activity conducted in a school building or public and commercial building to:

- Determine the presence or location of friable or non-friable ACBM or suspected ACBM, or

- To assess the condition of friable or non-friable ACBM or suspected ACBM by visual or physical examination, or by collecting samples.

Inspection includes re-inspections of friable and non-friable known or assumed ACBM, which had been identified in a prior inspection. It should be noted that ASHARA does not require inspections of public and commercial, but does require the use of accredited personnel

NATIONAL EMISSION STANDARDS FOR HAZARDOUS AIR POLLUTANT'S (NESHAP)

EPA's rules concerning the application, removal and disposal of asbestos-containing materials were issued under NESHAP. Also included in NESHAP are rules concerning manufacturing, spraying and fabrication of asbestos-containing material. NESHAP was revised November 20, 1990 to clarify requirements regarding removal and disposal of asbestos-containing materials. Provisions of NESHAP, which affect Building Inspectors are presented below.

NESHAP Definitions (selected):

Category I non-friable ACM: asbestos-containing packings, gaskets, resilient floor covering and asphalt roofing products containing more than 1% asbestos. (Category I non-friable ACM has been interpreted to include pliable asbestos-containing sealants and mastics since they exhibit many of the same characteristics of Category I non-friable asbestos-containing materials)

Category II Non-friable ACM: any material, excluding Category I non-friable ACM, containing more than 1% asbestos that, when dry, cannot be crumbled, pulverized, or reduced to powder by hand pressure. (Example: asbestos-cement products.)

Friable asbestos: any material containing more than 1% asbestos that, when dry, can be crumble d, pulverized, or reduced to powder by hand pressure.

Regulated asbestos-containing material (RACM): A) friable asbestos material, b) Category I non-friable ACM that has become friable, c) Category I non-friable ACM

Category I nonfriable ACM that will be or has been subjected to sanding, grinding, cutting, or abrading, or d) Category II nonfriable ACM that has a high probability of becoming or has become crumbled, pulverized, or reduced to powder by the forced expected to act on the material in the course of demolition or renovation operations regulated by subpart §61.141 of 40 CFR 61 (NESHAP Revision, Final Rule).

What are the inspection requirements of NESHAP?
- NESHAP requires a thorough inspection for friable and nonfriable ACM within building or facility prior to any demolition activity.
- Prior to any renovation activity, a thorough inspection for friable and nonfriable ACM must be conducted within the portion of the building or facility being renovated.

All inspections (including NESHAP inspections) must be done by an accredited inspector as required by AHERA or ASHARA (see discussion of ASHARA in this section).

What analytical method(s) are required to determine asbestos content of a material?
- The analytical method specified in Appendix A, subpart F, 40 CFR part 763 section 1 is Polarized Light Microscopy (PLM). This method is published as an appendix to the "Friable Asbestos-containing Material in Schools; Identification and Notification" rule (1982). (NOTE: EPA has published "Method for the Determination of Asbestos in Bulk Building Materials, EPA/600/R-93/116, July 1993. While the "Interim Method" continues to be the EPA compliance monitoring method and must be used for AHERA and NESHAP monitoring, the agency is considering replacing the Interim Method with this newer, improved procedure. Any change in the status of either method will be published in the *Federal Register*.)
- If the asbestos content is less than 10% as determined by a method other than point counting by PLM, verify the asbestos content by point counting using PLM. (See interpretive memo issued by EPA regarding point counting of samples- Exhibit L-2.)

The asbestos NESHAP regulation also includes specific notification, work practice, packaging, labeling, and disposal requirements.

ASBESTOS: MANUFACTURE, IMPORTATION, PROCESSING, AND DISTRIBUTION IN COMMERCE PROHIBITIONS; FINAL RULE (BAN AND PHASE OUT RULE)

SECTION L: REGULATORY REVIEW

This rule, was phased in over a seven year period beginning in 1990, prohibited the manufacture, importation, processing, and distribution of certain commercial available asbestos-containing products. This rule would have effectively banned the use of nearly 95% of all asbestos products used in the United States, with the exception of products for which no acceptable substitute has been found, and certain products for military use.

EPA has adopted separate dates for the banning of the manufacture, importation, and processing of asbestos-containing products, and for the distribution of asbestos-containing products in commerce. However, this regulation was vacated by the Fifth circuit court of Appeals in October, 1991. EPA appealed the court's decision and the appeal was rejected on November 27, 1991.

The court did not allow EPA to ban new use of certain asbestos-containing products and those products that were not being manufactured, imported, or processed on the date the final rule was issued (July 12, 1989). EPA issued a notice in the *Federal Register* that requested information on the status of 14 product categories included in the rule that were not being manufactured, processed, or imported when the final rule was published. Based on the research conducted by EPA, and information provided by commenters, EPA published in the June 28, 1994 *Federal Register* the following six products which are still subject to the Ban and Phase-out Rule:
- Corrugated pager
- Rollboard
- Commercial paper
- Specialty paper
- Flooring felt, and
- New uses of asbestos

EPA WORKER PROTECTION RULE

This regulation extends worker protection standards to state and local employees who perform asbestos work and who are not covered by the OSHA Asbestos Standards, or by a state OSHA plan. The Rule currently parallels 1986 OSHA requirements and covers medical examinations, air monitoring and reporting, protective equipment, work practices, and recordkeeping. This regulation is the process of being revised to include the amendments made to the OSHA asbestos standards since 1986.

OSHA ASBESTOS STANDARDS

The Occupational Health and Safety Administration has established three sets of regulations which address asbestos exposure:

29 CFR 1910.1001- General Industry
29 CFR 1926.1101- Construction Industry
29 CFR 1910.134- Use of Respirators (General)

The construction industry standard covers employees engaged in demolition and construction, and the following related activities likely to involve asbestos exposure: removal, encapsulation, alteration, repair, maintenance, installation, spill/emergency clean-up, transportation, disposal, and storage of ACM. The general industry standards cover all the other operations where exposure to asbestos is possible, including exposure to occupants of buildings which contain ACM. In most cases, however, levels of airborne asbestos are not expected to reach the exposure standards in these buildings.

In general, OSHA coverage extends to all private sector employers and employees in the 50 states and all territories under federal jurisdiction. Those not covered under the standard include: self-employed persons, certain state and local government employees, and federal employees covered under other federal statuses. Persons engaged in inspection, management planning, and other asbestos-related work fall under OSHA's Construction Industry Standard, which is discussed below.

To enforce its standards, OSHA is authorized to conduct workplace inspections. In addition, employees have the right to file and OSHA complaint without fear of punishment from the employer. In turn, employees have the responsibility to follow all safety and health rules. OSHA may not conduct a warrantless inspection without the employer's consent. Citations are issued by OSHA during an inspection if the compliance officer finds a standard being violated. The citation informs the employer and employees of the regulations or standards alleged to have been violated and of the proposed length of time for correction. Monetary penalties may also be imposed.

What is OSHA's definition of asbestos-containing material?
- Any material containing more than 1% asbestos.

How does OSHA define Presumed Asbestos-Containing Material (PACM)?
- PACM is thermal system insulation and surfacing material found in buildings constructed no later than 1980.

What are OSHA's classifications of work activities?
- Class I asbestos work includes the removal of thermal system insulation and surfacing ACM and PACM.
- Class II asbestos work includes the removal of ACM which is not thermal system insulation or surfacing material. This includes removal of floor tile, roofing products, construction mastics, etc.
- Class III asbestos work means repair and maintenance operations where ACM is likely to be disturbed.

- Class IV asbestos work includes maintenance and custodial work during which employees contact but do not disturb ACM and PACM, and activities to clean up waste and debris generated by Class I, II, and III activities.

What are the OSHA asbestos exposure limits?
- The permissible exposure limit, (PEL), is 0.1 fibers per cubic centimeter (f/cc) of air, time weighted average, (TWA). TWA means exposure concentration averaged over an 8 hour period.
- An excursion limit (EL) of 1.0 f/cc over a 30 minute TWA.

When are employees required to wear respirators?
- During all Class I asbestos jobs.
- During all Class II work where the ACM is not removed in a substantially intact manner.
- During all Class II and Class II work which is not performed using wet methods.
- During all Class II and Class III work where an employers has not conducted a negative exposure assessment.
- During all III work where TSI or surfacing ACM or PACM is being disturbed.
- During all Class IV work done within a regulated area where other workers are required to wear a respirator.
- During all work when an employee is exposed above the PEL or EL
- In emergencies.

What is a negative initial exposure assessment?
- A demonstration by an employer which indicates employee exposure during an operation is expected to be consistently below the PEL and EL.

What steps must be taken by an employer if an employee is required to wear a negative-pressure respirator?
- Establish a medical surveillance program
- Institute an employee training program.
- Establish a respiratory protection program.

What steps must be taken by an employer if employees are exposed to airborne asbestos at or above the PEL?
- Establish a respiratory protection program.
- Daily personal air sampling to record employee exposure to asbestos must be undertaken. (If air-supplied respirators, operated in a pressure-demand mode or other positive pressure mode are being worn this sampling is not required.)
- Employees must be notified as soon as possible, in writing, of the results of air sampling.

- The employer must establish a regulated area where concentrations of airborne asbestos exceed the PEL.
- Access to the regulated area is to be limited.
- Eating, smoking, drinking, and gum chewing are prohibited in the regulated area.
- A designated competent person must monitor the integrity of the area and enforce the above requirements.

What steps must be taken by an employer if employees are exposed to airborne asbestos at or above the EL?
- The same requirements which are triggered by the PEL.

What is the definition of " <u>competent person</u>"?
- An individual capable of identifying asbestos hazards and selecting the appropriate control strategy for asbestos exposure, and
- One who has authority to take corrective action to eliminate the hazards.

What are the responsibilities of the "competent person"?
- Set up the regulated area
- Determine the need for the negative-pressure enclosure and ensure its integrity.
- Control entry to and exit from the enclosure and/or regulated area.
- Supervise all Class I and Class II activity.
- Supervise employees working within a restricted area wear the appropriate personal protective equipment.
- Ensure that engineering controls in use are functioning properly.

What engineering and/or housekeeping controls are required to achieve compliance with exposure standards?
- <u>HEPA</u> filter ventilation systems and vacuum cleaners;
- Wet methods (wetting agents, cleaning processes);
- Prompt clean up and disposal of asbestos-containing waste and debris

What hazard communication measures are required?
-
-
-
-

- Before any work which is regulated by OSHA can be conducted, the building and facility owners must identify the presence, location, and quantity of ACM and/or PACM.

- Warning signs to identify a regulated area must be posted. Where respirators are required in a regulated area, warning sign must be posted.

- The employer shall ensure that employees working in and contiguous to regulated areas comprehend these warning signs. This may be accomplished through the use of foreign language wording, pictographs, and graphics.

- Labels are to be attached to any product containing asbestos and to all waste containers. Warning labels must contain the following words and be Black, White, and Red in color:

What training is required under the OSHA standard?
- OSHA bases its training requirements on the class of activity an individual will perform:
    - Class I activities must be conducted by persons accredited as asbestos abatement workers under the EPA Model Accreditation Plan;
    - Class II activities which involve asbestos-containing roofing materials, flooring materials, siding materials, ceiling tiles, or transit panels must be conducted by persons trained in the topics outlined by OSHA, including hands-on minimum of 8 hours. Other Class II training must cover the OSHA required topics, include hands-on training, and cover the OSHA work practices and engineering control requirements detailed for Class II work. There is no specified course length for this Class II training.
    - Class III activities must be performed by persons with 16-hour training for maintenance and custodial workers as outlined under AHERA;
    - Class IV activities must be performed by personnel who receive 2 hour awareness training as outlined under AHERA;
    - Class IV activities must be performed by personnel who receive 2 hour awareness training as outlined under AHERA;
    - Competent Persons must be trained as Contractors/Supervisors or Project Designers under EPA's Model Accreditation Plan for Class I and II work, and is trained under EPA's 16 hour maintenance and custodial training program for Class III and IV work.
- Employers must provide employees with training that covers the following topics:
    - Methods of recognizing asbestos;

160

o The health effects associated with asbestos exposure;
o Relationship between smoking and exposure to asbestos;
o Work practices and control measures to minimize exposure
o Purpose, proper use, fitting, and limitations of respirators
o Medical surveillance program requirements
o The OSHA standard
o The availability of self-help smoking cessation program material
o The requirements for posting signs and affixing labels and the meaning of the required legends for such signs and labels

Who is to be covered by a medical surveillance program?
- All employees who for 30 or more days per year are engaged in Class I, II, and III work or are exposed to fiber levels at or above the PEL or EL.
- All employees who are required to wear negative-pressure respirators. (Medical surveillance is covered in the respiratory protection section Section J.
- What recordkeeping requirements are specified under OSHA?
- Employee medical surveillance records must be maintained for duration of employment plus 30 years.
- All employee exposure sampling data must be retained for 30 years.
- Training materials must be retained 1 year after termination of employment for each employee.
- All records must be made available to the employee, to OSHA, and with permission to the employee's union representative.
- Special provisions are established for records when an employer goes out of business.

The OSHA construction Standard affects the Building Inspector as well as asbestos abatement contractors and workers. If levels of airborne fibers to which Building Inspectors are exposed exceed the PEL or excursion limit, medical surveillance programs must be established. This is also the case if employees of a firm conducting building inspections for asbestos wear negative-pressure respirators. The only exception is self-employed persons.

Any employer, large or small, who falls under the jurisdiction of OSHA must provide:
- Respirators at no cost to employees
- Protective clothing, when appropriate at no cost to employees
- A medical surveillance program at no cost to employees
- Awareness training (communication of potential hazards)

The OSHA respirator rule specifies what type of respirators must be worn for different levels of contaminants in the air. A half or full face mask negative-pressure air purifying respirator with high efficiency particulate air (HEPA) filters should be sufficient for conducting inspections and collecting bulk samples. Exceptions requiring a higher level of protection would be extremely dusty or contaminated areas such as crawl spaces.

In most bulk sampling situations, fiber levels are not expected to reach the PEL or excursion limit. However, the only way to ascertain this is to undertake extensive personal air monitoring. In the absence of such data, it is advisable to follow the prudent course and comply with the OSHA standards.

STATE AND LOCAL REGULATIONS

Several provisions in AHERA and ASHARA encourage states to develop their own regulatory programs. For example, states are encouraged to establish and operate training and certification programs for the various categories of asbestos professionals, as long as the programs are at least as stringent as AHERA's Model Plan. In addition, some states have established requirements that exceed EPA's in the area of notification of abatement actions, abatement work practices, and transportation and disposal of asbestos-contaminated waste. Inspectors/Management Planners should consult state and local regulatory agencies in their areas.

The flowing pages outline federal agency regulations both by year and regulatory action.

EXHIBIT L-1
CHRONOLOGY OF ASBESTOS LEGISLATION

YEAR	EPA	OSHA	OTHER
1971	Asbestos listed as hazardous air pollutant.	Existing occupational exposure standard 5 f/cc	
1973	Standard for milling, manufacturing, and building demolition		
1973	No visible emissions		
1975	No visible emissions standard extended to waste collection, disposal, and processing industries not previously covered.		
1976		Occupational exposure standard lowered to 2 f/cc	
1977			Consumer Product Safety Commission prohibition of

			asbestos in patching compounds and emberizing agents.
1978	All friable spray-on material prohibited, all demolition and renovation covered by no visible emissions standard (EPA/NESHAP)		Controls regarding transport of friable ACM (DOT)
1979	Technical assistance program to schools initiated to identify and control friable ACM		Controls regarding transport of friable ACM (DOT)
1982	Identification and notification of friable ACM in schools rule (EPA/TSCA)		
1984	EPA/NESHAP standard formally recognized Asbestos School Hazard loan and grant program to help eliminate hazards		
1986	AHERA	Construction Industry Standard issued. Permissible exposure level lowered to 0.2 f/cc and action level of 0.1 f/cc established.	
1987	TSCA amended to reflect AHERA		
	Worker protection rule		
1988		Amendment of general and construction industry asbestos standards to include 30-minute excursion limit (1.0 f/cc)	
1989	Ban & Phase-Out Rule		
1990	Extensive NESHAP revisions including Category I & II nonfriable material definitions, point	Court-ordered amendments to asbestos standard for the construction	DOT Hazardous Materials Regulations (HMR) 49 CFR Part 107 et.

	counting, and waste disposal manifests.	industry regarding informing employees of the hazards of smoking and working with asbestos; employee sign comprehension.	Al. published based on UN standards. Included new asbestos classification, hazard communication, packaging, and handling requirements.
1991	Fifth Circuit Court of Appeals vacates most of Ban & Phase-out Rule		
1992	ASHAA reauthorized (ASHARA), requiring accreditation of designers, inspectors, contractors/supervisors, and workers involved in asbestos detection and remediation in public and commercial buildings.		DOT HRM revised with less stringent requirements when shipping friable asbestos within the United States.
	EPA issues draft list of asbestos products still covered by Ban & Phase-Out Rule.		
1993	EPA published list of asbestos-containing products which are banned from manufacture, importation, processing, and distribution.		
1994	ASHARA Interim Final Rule published including revisions to MAP	Revisions to General and Construction Industry Standards and Issuance of Shipyard Standard	
1996		Interpretative letters clarify bulk sample analysis of drywall or gypsum board, joint compound, and tape be performed separately (where feasible), if any of the	

		layers contain >1% worker protection is required.	
1998		Interpretative letters clarify that bulk sampling procedures are considered class III operations and hard wall/ceiling plasters and stucco are not considered surfacing materials	
1999	Respiratory Protection Standard revised to require fit testing for all tight fitting masks and to be performed at least annually, the assigned protection factors for qualitative fit tests dropped to 10 x's and the approval of mobile quantitative fit testing devices.		
2000	Worker Protection Rule amended to incorporate both Construction & General Industry Asbestos Standards		

Your instructor will provide you with any additional regulations.

CLARIFICATION OF NESHAP REQUIREMENT TO PERFORM POINT COUNTING TO QUANTIFY ASBESTOS BELOW 10%

Since the amendment to the NESHAP for asbestos, November 20, 1990) there have been several questions regarding the interpretation of the point count rule. Also, several recommendations for improving the quantitative analysis of asbestos in bulk samples have been made. This clarification notice addresses these questions and discusses the recommendations. A discussion of important considerations related to the quantitative analysis of asbestos in bulk samples follows the clarification statements. This clarification applies to all regulated asbestos containing materials.

First, a sample in which no asbestos is detected by polarized light microscopy (PLM) does not have to be point counted. However, a minimum of three slide mounts should be prepared and examined in their entirety by PLM to determine if asbestos is present. This process should be carefully documented by the laboratory.

Second, if the analyst detects asbestos in the sample and estimates the amount by visual estimation to be less than 10%, the owner or operator of the building may (1) elect to assume the amount to be greater than 1% and treat the material as asbestos-containing material or (2) require verification of the amount by point counting.

Third, if a result obtained by point count is different from a result obtained by visual estimation, the point count result will be used.

DISCUSSION

The NESHAP for asbestos (requires that when the asbestos content of a bulk material is determined using procedures outlined in the interim method (40 CFR Part 763, Appendix A to Subpart F), and the asbestos content is estimated to be less than 10% by a method other than point counting, the quantitative analysis must be repeated using the point count technique. This action was taken after several reports of data from split samples analyzed by visual estimation by two or more laboratories produced conflicting results which made it difficult to determine if a sample should be classified as an asbestos-containing material. The materials were reanalyzed by point count and by interlaboratory exchange of prepared samples resulting in a consistent set of data. A review of data from performance audits indicated an unacceptable number of false negatives (reporting the sample as containing less than 1% asbestos for asbestos-containing samples containing greater than 1% asbestos) and an unacceptable number of false positives (reporting the sample as containing greater than 1% asbestos for samples containing less than 1% asbestos).

The Office of Research and Development (EPA/ORD) informally interviewed laboratories to determine the cause of these errors and learned that: (1) some laboratories did not view a sufficient amount of the sample to detect asbestos when present or failed to properly identify the asbestos component, resulting in false negatives and (2) some laboratories employed arbitrary rules for determining quantity, such as "one fiber detected is considered to be greater than 1%", resulting in false positives. Several round-robin studies and eighteen rounds of performance audit data indicate nearly all laboratories greatly overestimate the amount of asbestos using visual estimation techniques which are not related to standard materials of known composition. Because these false negatives and false positives result in either operations not being covered by NESHAP that should be or unnecessary expenditure of funds for abatement, respectively, the Agency believes that additional effort on the part of the laboratory is warranted.

It should be noted that samples in which no asbestos is detected during analysis by polarized light microscopy (PLM) do not have to be point counted. However, a minimum of three slide mounts should be prepared and examined in their entirety by PLM to determine if asbestos is present. Point counting will not improve the probability of detection of asbestos where no asbestos has been detected by PLM unless the analyst has only made a very cursory examination of the sample. In fact, the detection limit for the point counting method would be higher (less likelihood of detection) than that expected by visual estimation due to the fact that the only asbestos fibers counted are those that fall directly under the reticle index (cross line or point array), whereas (in theory) all fibers are observed during visual estimation.

When asbestos is observed to be above the laboratory blank level during PLM analysis, but less than 1% asbestos counts are recorded during point counting, the laboratory should report the sample contains trace asbestos. Also, false negatives that result from (1) misidentification of asbestos fibers as nonasbestos or (2) due to the inability of the microscopist to detect and confirm the presence of asbestos will not be corrected by the point counting technique. Accurate results by point counting are obviously dependent on correct identification of fibers. A similar relationship is true for false positives, although it would be expected that point counting could improve quantitative results, given the pervasive tendency of laboratories to overestimate asbestos content, especially at the lower concentrations (less than 10%). However, the laboratory should take care to examine a sufficient amount of any sample to be sure that it does not contain asbestos. If the sample is not homogenous, some homogenization procedure should be performed to ensure that slide preparations made from small pinch samples are representative of the total sample. A minimum of three slide mounts should be examined to determine the asbestos content by visual area estimation. Each slide should be scanned in its entirety and the relative proportions of asbestos to nonasbestos noted. It is suggested that the amount of asbestos compared to the amount of nonasbestos material be recorded in several fields on each slide and the results be compared to data derived from the analysis of calibration materials having similar textures and asbestos content.

The parties legally responsible for a building (owner or operator) may take a conservative approach to being regulated by the asbestos NESHAP. The responsible party may choose to act as through the building material is an asbestos containing material (greater than 1% asbestos) at any level of asbestos content (even less than 1% asbestos). Thus, if the analyst detects asbestos in the sample and estimates the amount to be less than 10% by visual estimation, the parties legally responsible (owner or operator) for the building may (1) elect to assume the amount to be greater than 1% and treat the material as regulated asbestos-containing material or (2) require verification of the amount by point counting.

The interim method states that asbestos shall be quantified using point counting or an equivalent estimation technique. The Agency (ORD) has been conducting research to determine procedures for defining "equivalent estimation". Recent studies have suggested that the use of gravimetrically prepared standard materials, in conjunction with quantitative techniques, can be used to improve the analyst's ability to estimate asbestos quantity. A procedure for the formulation of calibration materials and quality assurance (QA) procedures for their use has been drafted and is being tested. The Agency believes that use of such materials and QA procedures, as well as other objective measurement techniques, have the potential to greatly improve quantitative estimates of asbestos, especially in the range below 10%. If the research proves these procedures to be worthy, the Agency will consider proposing a revised method. A draft of the proposed procedure will be circulated to all NVLAP labs for comment when it has been approved internally.

SUMMARY OF ASBESTOS LAWS AND REGULATIONS

I.   Asbestos Laws and Regulations

This page provides a listing of the laws and regulations pertaining to asbestos implemented by the EPA and certain other federal agencies.

EPA Asbestos-Related Laws

- The Asbestos Hazard Emergency Response Act (AHERA)
- The Asbestos Information Act (AIA)
- The Asbestos School Hazard Abatement Reauthorization Act (ASHARA)
- The Clean Air Act (CAA)
- Safe Drinking Water Act (SDWA)

EPA Asbestos Regulations

- Asbestos-Containing Materials in Schools Rule (40 CFR Part 763, Subpart E)
- Asbestos Worker Protection Rule (40 CFR Part 763, Subpart G)
- Asbestos Ban and Phaseout Rule (Remanded) (40 CFR Part 763, Subpart I)
- Asbestos National Emission Standard for Hazardous Air Pollutants (NESHAP) Regulations (40 CFR Part 61, Subpart M)

Other Federal Agencies with Asbestos Regulations

- Occupational Safety and Health Administration (OSHA)
- Consumer Product Safety Commission (CPSC)
- Mine Safety and Health Administration (MSHA)

168

SECTION L: REGULATORY REVIEW

1. EPA Asbestos-Related Laws

The Asbestos Hazard Emergency Response Act (AHERA) (Toxic Substances Control Act (TSCA) Title II)

This law required EPA to promulgate regulations (e.g., the Asbestos-Containing Materials in Schools Rule) requiring local educational agencies to inspect their school buildings for asbestos-containing building material, prepare asbestos management plans and perform asbestos response actions to prevent or reduce asbestos hazards. AHERA also tasked EPA with developing a model plan for states for accrediting persons conducting asbestos inspection and corrective-action activities at schools. The Toxic Substances Control Act defines asbestos as the asbestiform varieties of: chrysotile (serpentine); crocidolite (riebeckite); amosite (cummingtonite/grunerite); anthophyllite; tremolite; and actinolite.
TSCA Subchapter II: Asbestos Hazard Emergency Response (15 U.S.C. § 2641-2656)

Asbestos Information Act (Public Law 100-577)

This law helped to provide transparency and identify the companies making certain types of asbestos-containing products by requiring manufacturers to report production to the EPA.
February 13, 1990 Federal Register Notice: Disclosure of the Production of Asbestos-Containing Materials

Asbestos School Hazard Abatement Reauthorization Act (ASHARA)

This law extended funding for the asbestos abatement loan and grant program for schools. ASHARA also directed EPA to increase the number of training hours required for the training disciplines under the Asbestos Model Accreditation Plan (MAP) and to expand the accreditation requirements to cover asbestos abatement projects in all public and commercial buildings in addition to schools.

- Asbestos School Hazard Abatement Reauthorization Act of 1990
- Asbestos Model Accreditation Plan
- February 3, 1994 Federal Register Notice: Asbestos Model Accreditation Plan

Clean Air Act (CAA) (42 USC § 7401 et seq.)

This law defines the EPA's responsibilities for protecting and improving the nation's air quality and the stratospheric ozone layer and includes provisions for the EPA to set national emission standards for hazardous air pollutants, including asbestos.

- Section 112- National Emission Standards for Hazardous Air Pollutants

Safe Drinking Water Act (SDWA)

The Safe Drinking Water Act (SDWA) is the federal law that helps ensure the quality of Americans' drinking water. Under the SDWA, EPA sets standards for drinking water quality and oversees the states, localities, and water suppliers who implement those standards.

2.   EPA Asbestos Regulations

Asbestos-Containing Materials in Schools Rule

Pursuant to the Asbestos Hazard Emergency Response Act (AHERA), the Asbestos-Containing Materials in Schools rule requires local education agencies to inspect their school buildings for asbestos-containing building material, prepare asbestos management plans and perform asbestos response actions to prevent or reduce asbestos hazards. Public school districts and non-profit private schools, including charter schools and schools affiliated with religious institutions (collectively called local education agencies) are subject to the rule's requirements.

- Asbestos-Containing Materials in Schools Rule (40 CFR Part 763, Subpart E)
  - Interim Transmission Electron Microscopy (TEM) Analytical Methods (Appendix A to Subpart E of 40 CFR Part 763)
  - Asbestos Model Accreditation Plan (Appendix C to Subpart E of 40 CFR Part 763)
  - Transport and Disposal of Asbestos Waste (Appendix D to Subpart E of 40 CFR Part 763)
  - Interim Method of the Determination of Asbestos in Bulk Insulation Samples (Appendix E to Subpart E of 40 CFR Part 763)

EPA Asbestos Worker Protection Rule

Through the authority of Section 6 of the Toxic Substances Control Act (TSCA) the EPA extended worker protection requirements to state and local government employees involved in asbestos work who were not previously covered by the the Occupational Safety and Health Administration's (OSHA) asbestos regulations.

- 40 CFR Part 763, Subpart G – Asbestos Worker Protection

Asbestos Ban and Phaseout Rule (Remanded)

On July 12, 1989, the EPA issued a final rule banning most asbestos-containing products. In 1991, this regulation was overturned by the Fifth Circuit Court of Appeals. However, as a result of the Court's decision, only a few asbestos-containing products remain banned. .

- 40 CFR Part 763, Subpart I -- Prohibition of the Manufacture, Importation, Processing and Distribution in Commerce of Certain Asbestos-Containing Products; Labeling Requirements

170

Asbestos National Emission Standards for Hazardous Air Pollutants (NESHAP)

The asbestos NESHAP regulations specify work practices for asbestos to be followed during demolitions and renovations of all structures, installations, and buildings (excluding residential buildings that have four or fewer dwelling units). The regulations require the owner of the building or the operator to notify the appropriate state agency before any demolition, or before any renovations of buildings that could contain a certain threshold amount of asbestos or asbestos-containing material. In addition, particular manufacturing and fabricating operations either cannot emit visible emissions into the outside air or must follow air cleaning procedures, as well as follow certain requirements when removing asbestos-containing waste.

- 40 CFR Part 61, Subpart M (Complete Rule)
- 40 CFR §61.145—Standard for demolition and renovation
- 40 CFR §61.150—Standard for waste disposal for manufacturing, fabricating, demolition, renovation, and spraying operations

3.   **Other Federal Agencies with Asbestos Regulations**

Occupational Safety and Health Administration (OSHA)

OSHA oversees the working conditions for U.S. workers by implementing and managing occupational safety and health standards. The following regulations pertain to handling asbestos in the workplace.

- Asbestos General Standard—Specification of permissible exposure limits, engineering controls, worker training, labeling, respiratory protection, and disposal of asbestos waste
    - 29 CFR 1910.1001
- Asbestos Construction Standard—Covers construction work involving asbestos, including work practices during demolition and renovation, worker training, disposal of asbestos waste, and specification of permissible exposure limits
    - 29 CFR 1926.1101

SECTION L: REGULATORY REVIEW

Consumer Product Safety Commission (CPSC)

The CPSC protects consumers and families from consumer products that pose a fire, electrical, chemical, or mechanical hazard or can injure children. Below are the following CPSC bans or restrictions on asbestos-containing products:

- Emberizing Materials
  - 16 CFR Part 1305
- Patching Compounds
  - 16 CFR Part 1304
- Asbestos Containing Garments for General Use
  - 16 CFR § 1500.17(a)(7)

Mine Safety and Health Administration (MSHA)

MSHA is responsible for overseeing the safety and health of miners in the U.S. The following MSHA regulations apply to asbestos in mines:

- Surface Mines: exposure limits, engineering controls, and respiratory protection measures for workers in surface mines
  - 30 CFR part 56, subpart D
- Underground Mines: exposure limits, engineering controls, and respiratory protection measures for workers in underground mines
  - 30 CFR part 57, subpart D

PURPOSE:

The purpose of the inspection field trip s to provide hands-on training to Building Inspectors. The field trip will consist of an actual walk-through inspection of a building with an instructor present to serve as an on-site resource person.

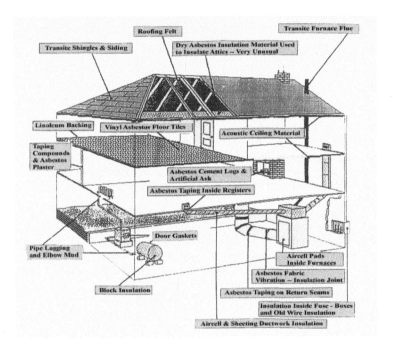

ORGANIZATION

Course participants will be divided into small groups prior to going out into the field. Each group will be transported to the field inspection site accompanied by an instructor. Following the inspection, groups will return to the classroom for a discussion of the field exercise.

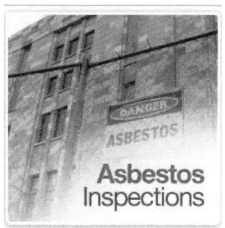

FIELD ACTIVITIES

The field exercise will provide course participants with an opportunity to put into practice the concepts addressed in class. The exercise will focus on:

1. Identification of areas/surfaces/systems where ACM is likely to be found.
2. Identification of materials which should be inventoried but not sampled.
3. Delineation of homogenous sampling areas.
4. Development of sampling plans (i.e., determination of the number of samples to be collected and selection of sample locations).
5. Documentation of the sampling plan and sample collection (actual sampling will not be done).
6. Physical assessment of suspect material.

Acoustical Insulation — The general application or use of asbestos for the control of sound due to its lack of reverberant surfaces.

Acoustical Tile — A finishing material in a building usually found in the ceiling or walls for the purpose of noise control.

Actinolite — One of six naturally occurring asbestos minerals. It is not normally used commercially.

Addenda — Changes made to working drawings and specifications for a building before the work is bid.

AHERA — Asbestos Hazard Emergency Response Act. U.S. EPA

Algorithm — A formal numerical procedure for assessing suspect material; results are given a numerical score.

Alveoli — Located in clusters around the respiratory bronchioles of the lungs, this is the area in which true respiration takes place.

Amosite — An asbestiform mineral of the amphibole group. It is the second most commonly used for of asbestos in the U.S. Also known as brown asbestos.

Amphibole — One of the two major groups of minerals from which the asbestiform minerals are derived—distinguished by their chain-like crystal structure and chemical composition. Amosite and Crocidolite are examples of amphibole minerals.

Anthophyllite — One of six naturally occurring asbestos minerals. It is of limited commercial value.

Asbestos — A generic name given to a number of naturally occurring hydrated mineral silicates that possess a unique crystalline structure, are incombustible in air, and are separable into fibers. Asbestos includes the asbestiform varieties of chrysotile (serpentine); Crocidolite (riebeckite); amosite (cummingtonite-grunerite); anthopbhyllite; tremolite, and actinolite.

Asbestos Bodies — Coated asbestos fibers often seen in the lungs of asbestos-exposure victims.

SECTION N: ASBESTOS GLOSSARY

Asbestos-Containing
Building Material (ACBM)

Surfacing ACM, thermal system insulation ACM, or miscellaneous ACM that is found in or on interior structural members or other parts of a school building (AHERA definition).

Asbestos-Containing
Material

Any material or product which contains more than 1 percent asbestos (AHERA, OSHA definition).

Asbestosis

A non-malignant, progressive, irreversible lung disease caused by the inhalation of asbestos dust and characterized by diffuse fibrosis

ASHARA

Asbestos School Hazard Abatement Reauthorization Act. U.S. EPA regulation enacted November 28, 1992 which extended accreditation requirements for inspectors, contractor/supervisors, designers, and workers to public and commercial buildings.

Breeching

A duct which transports combustion gases from a boiler or heater to a chimney or stack. Also called a flue.

Building Inspector

A person who conducts a survey of a building for the presence of asbestos-containing materials. Must be accredited under AHERA and ASHARA regulations.

Bulk Sample

Sample of bulk material; in the case of asbestos, suspect material.

Category I Nonfriable
ACM

Asbestos-containing packing's, gaskets, resilient floor covering and asphalt roofing products containing more than 1% asbestos.

Category II Nonfriable
ACM

Any material, excluding Category I nonfriable ACM containing more than 1% asbestos that, when dry, cannot be crumbled, pulverized, or reduced to powder by hand pressure. Example: asbestos/cement products.

Cementitious ACM

Asbestos-containing materials that re densely packed, granular and are generally nonfriable.

Chain-of custody

Formal procedures for tracking samples and insuring their integrity.

Change Order

A change to construction documents after a contract for construction has been signed.

Chrysotile	The only asbestiform mineral of the serpentine group. It is the most common form of asbestos used in buildings. Also known as white asbestos.
Certified Industrial Hygienist (CIH)	An industrial hygienist who has been granted certification by the American Board of Industrial Hygiene.
Cilia	Tiny hair-like structures in the windpipe and bronchi of the lung passages which beat upward and that help force undesirable particles, fibers, and liquids up and out of the lungs.
Claims-Made Insurance	A from of insurance in which a claim is allowed only if the insurance is in effect when the claim is made, that is, when the injury or effect is observed.
Contract Documents	Legally binding building drawings and specifications. Also called construction documents.
Crocidolite	The strongest of the asbestos minerals. An asbestiform mineral of the amphibole group. It is of minor commercial value in the U.S. Blue asbestos.
Damaged Friable Surfacing (Miscellaneous) Material	Friable surfacing (miscellaneous) ACM which has deteriorated or sustained physical injury such that the internal structure (cohesion) of the material is inadequate or, if applicable, which as delaminated such that the bond to the substrate (adhesion) is inadequate or which for any other reason lacks fiber cohesion or adhesion qualities. Such damage or deterioration may be illustrated by the separation of ACM into layers; separation of ACM from the substrate; flaking, blistering, or crumbling of ACM surface; water damage; significant or repeated water stains, scrapes, gauges, mars or other signs of physical injury on the ACM. Asbestos debris originating from the ACBM in question may also indicate damage (AHERA definition).
Damaged or Significantly Damaged Thermal System Insulation	Thermal system insulation on pipes, boilers, tanks, ducts, and other thermal system insulation equipment which has lost its structural integrity, or whose covering, in whole or in part, is crushed, water-stained, gouged, punctured, missing, or not intact such that it is not able to contain fibers. Damage may

be further illustrated by occasional punctures, gouges, or other signs of physical injury to ACM; occasional water damage on the protective coverings/jackets; or exposed ACM ends on joints. Asbestos debris originating from the ACBM in question may also indicate damage (AHERA definition).

Dose-Response Effect	The relationship between the amount of pollutant a person is exposed to (dose) and the increase risk of disease (effect). Usually the greater the dose, the greater the effect.
Electrical Systems	The system of wires, lights, power generation equipment, and related facilities to produce, convey, and utilize electrical power in a building.
Encapsulation	The use of an agent to seal the surface (bridging encapsulant) or penetrate the bulk (penetrating encapsulant) of ACM.
Enclosure	A resilient structure, built (or sprayed) around ACM designed to prevent disturbance and contain released fibers.
Epidemiology	The study of causes, occurrence, and distribution of disease throughout a population.
Errors and Omissions Insurance	A type of insurance which protects professionals for mistakes they may make in contracted plans and recommendations.
Excursion Limit (EL)	A level of airborne fibers specified by OSHA as a short term excursion level. It is currently 1.0 fibers per cubic centimeter (f/cc) of air, 30-minute time-weighted average, as measured by phase contrast microscopy.
f/cc	Fibers per cubic centimeters of air
Fireproofing	Spray- or trowel-applied fire resistant materials.
Friable	Any materials that can be crumbled pulverized or reduced to powder by hand pressure when dry.
Functional Spaces	Spatially distinct units within a building which contain identifiable populations of building occupants.
General Liability	A type of insurance which covers the insured for

Insurance	damage to property and person caused by his or her own negligence.
Hazard Assessment	The interpretation and evaluation of physical assessment data in order to set abatement priorities and rank areas for response actions. These priorities and rankings are based on anticipated exposure to asbestos fibers.
Heating, Ventilating And Air Conditioning (HVAC) system	The system of pipes, ducts, and equipment (air conditioners, chillers, heaters, boilers, pumps, fans) used to heat, cool, move and filter air in a building. HVAC systems are also known as mechanical systems.
High Efficiency Particulate Air (HEPA)	A type of filter which is 99.97% efficient at filtering particles of 0.3 micrometers in diameter.
Homogeneous Sampling Area	An area of ACBM or suspect ACBM which appears similar throughout in terms of color, texture, and date of material application
Indemnify	To pay for or pay back. Indemnification clauses in contracts are intended to cover the cost of judgments and/or legal defenses in the event of litigation.
Industrial Hygienist	A professional qualified by education, training, and experience to recognize, evaluate, and develop controls for occupational health hazards.
Latency Period	The time between first exposure to a disease-causing agent and the appearance of the disease.
Liability	Being subject to legal action for one's behavior.
Local Education Agency (LEA)	Authority responsible for complying with AHERA. As defined in Section 198 of the Elementary and Secondary Education Act of 1965.
Lung Cancer	A malignant growth of abnormal cells in the lungs, specifically of the bronchi opening.
Macrophage	White blood cells which attack foreign substances in the body. The release of enzymes from these cells as they attack indigestible particles, such as asbestos, contributes to the creation of scar tissue in the lung.

SECTION N: ASBESTOS GLOSSARY

Management Plan	A plan for each LEA to control and manage ACBM (AHERA definition). Must be prepared by an EPA or state accredited Management Planner.
Management Planner	An individual that has completed an EPA or State approved course and passed an examination covering the development of management plans.
Mechanical Systems	See HVAC systems.
Mesothelioma	A relatively rare form of cancer which develops in the lining of the pleura or peritoneum with no known cure. It is almost always caused by exposure to asbestos.
Micrometer	One millionth of one meter.
Miscellaneous Material	Interior building material on structural components, structural members or fixtures, such as floor and ceiling tiles, and does not include surfacing material or thermal system insulation (AHERA definition).
MSHA	Mine Safety and Health Administration
Negative Pressure Respirators	Respirators which function by the wearer breathing in air through a filter.
Negative Pressure Respirator Fit Check	A form of qualitative fit testing in which the wearer covers the filters of a negative pressure, air-purifying respirator to check for leaks around the face seal.
NESHAP	National Emission Standards for Hazardous Air Pollutants-EPA Regulation 40 CFR subpart, part 61
NIOSH	The National Institute for Occupational Safety and Health which was established by the Occupational Safety and Health Act of 1970.
NIOSH/MSHA	The official approving agencies for respiratory protective equipment who test and certify respirators.
Occurrence Insurance	A form of insurance in which a claim in allowed regardless of when the claim is filed. For asbestos insurance, the "occurrence" could be the time of first exposure.
Operations and	Specific procedures and practices developed for the

SECTION N: ASBESTOS GLOSSARY

Maintenance Plan (O&M) interim control of asbestos-containing materials in buildings until it is removed.

OSHA The Occupational Safety and Health Administration which was created by the Occupational Safety and Health Act of 1970; serves as the enforcement agency for safety and health in the workplace environment

Permissible Exposure Unit (PEL) A level of airborne fibers specified by OSHA as an occupational exposure standard for asbestos. It is currently 0.1 fibers per cubic centimeter of air, 8-hour time-weighted average, as measured by phase contrast microscopy.

Phase Contrast Microscopy (PCM) An optical microscopic technique used for the counting of fibers in air samples, but which does not distinguish fiber types.

Physical Assessment Assessing suspect material to determine the current condition of the material and the potential for future disturbance.

Plenum A horizontal space designed to transport air in a building. Plenums are commonly the space between a dropped ceiling and the floor above.

Pleura The thin membrane surrounding the lungs, and which lines the internal surface of the chest cavity.

Plumbing System The system of pipes, valves, fittings, and related components designed to convey liquid or gas fluids throughout a building. Some piping may also be part of the HVAC system.

Point Counting A method of analyzing bulk samples whereby the sample is homogenized, placed on microscope slides and examined under a polarized light microscope. A point counting stage (or mechanical stage) and cross hair reticle are used for counting with only the particle(s) directly under the cross being counted (void space is not counted). A minimum of 400 counts should be made for each slide (several slides are examined).

Polarized Light An optical microscopy technique for analyzing bulk

Microscopy (PLM)	samples for asbestos in which the sample is illuminated with polarized light (light which vibrates in only one plane) to distinguish between different types of asbestos fibers by their shape and unique optical properties.
Positive Pressure Respirators	Respirators which function by blowing air or providing pressurized air to the wearer.
Positive Pressure Respirator Fit Check	A form of qualitative fit testing in which the wearer covers the exhalation valve of the negative pressure, air purifying respirator to check for leaks around the face seal.
Protection Factor (PF)	A number which reflects the degree of protection provided by a respirator. I tis calculated by dividing the concentration of contaminant outside the mask by concentration inside the mask.
Presumed ACM	Asbestos-containing thermal system insulation and surfacing materials found in a building constructed no later than 1980. (OSHA regulations)
Qualitative Fit Test	A method of testing a respirator's face-to-facepiece seal by covering the inhalation or exhalation valves and either breathing in or out to determine the presence of any leaks.
Quality Assurance	A program for collecting and analyzing additional samples of suspect material to check on the reliability of procedures.
Quantitative Fit Testing	Testing the fit of a respirator by calculating concentrations of contaminants inside and outside the mask. This requires the use of instruments.
Rales	Cracking sounds in the lower half of the lung; symptomatic of progressing asbestosis.
Random Sample	A samples drawn in such a way that there is no set pattern and is designed to give a true representation of the entire population or area.
Record Documents	Drawings and specifications which should reflect the way a building was actually constructed (sometimes referred to as "as-built drawings")

SECTION N: ASBESTOS GLOSSARY

Regulated Asbestos-Containing Material (RACM)	a) friable asbestos material, b) Category I nonfriable ACM that has become friable, c) Category I nonfriable ACM that will be or has been subjected to sanding, grinding, cutting, or abrading, or d) Category II nonfriable ACM that has a high probability of becoming or has become crumbled, pulverized or reduced to powder by the forces expected to act on the material in the course of demolition or renovation operations regulated by subpart §61.141 of 40 CFR Part 61 (NESHAP) Revision; Final Rule).
Respiration	The exchange of gases in the lungs.
Respiratory Protection Program	A set of procedures and equipment required by OSHA to be established by an employer which provides for the safe use of respirators on their job sites.
Respiratory Tract	The organs of the body which convey air to the blood, allow exchange of gases, and remove carbon dioxide.
Serpentine	One of the two major groups of minerals from which the asbestiform minerals are derived; distinguished by their tubular structure an chemical composition. Chrysotile is a serpentine mineral.
Shop Drawings	Detailed drawings of selected items used in the construction of a building that are drawn by the contractor, but reviewed by the architect/engineer responsible for designing the project.
Significantly Damaged Friable Surfacing (Miscellaneous) Material	Friable surfacing (miscellaneous) ACM in a functional space where damage is extensive and severe (AHERA definition).
Specifications	A written set of standards, procedures, and materials for the construction of a building.
Structural Member	Any load-supporting member such as beams and load supporting walls of a facility.
Submittals	Drawings or descriptive literature such as operating manuals transmitted to the building owner upon construction completion.
Substrate	The material or existing surface located under or behind the asbestos-containing material.

Surfacing Material	Material that is sprayed-on, troweled-on, or otherwise applied to surfaces, such as acoustical plaster on ceilings and fireproofing materials on structural members, or other materials on surfaces for acoustical, fireproofing, or other purposes (AHERA definition).
Synergistic	The combination of two effects which is greater than the sum of the two independent effects.
Thermal System Insulation	Material applied to pipes, fittings, boilers, breeching, tanks, ducts, or other interior structural components to prevent heat loss, or gain, or water condensation, or for other purposes.
Tort	A legal wrong, sometimes referred to as negligence.
Trachea	The main air tube into the lungs. Made up of cartilage and supported by cartilage rings, the trachea divides into two bronchi which lead into the lungs.
Transite™	A trade name for asbestos cement wallboard and sheeting.
Transmission Electron Microscopy (TEM)	A method of microscopic analysis which utilizes an electron beam that is focused onto a thin sample. As the beam penetrates (transmits) through the sample, the difference in densities produces an image on a fluorescent screen from which samples can be identified and counted. Used for analyzing air samples for asbestos.
Tremolite	One of six naturally occurring asbestos minerals. Tremolite has few commercial uses.
Working drawings	A set of drawings which reflect the intended construction and appearance of the building. Also known as building plans.
U.S. EPA	United States Environment Protection Agency. Created in 1970, the U.S. EPA is the federal promulgator and enforcement agency for environmental regulations.

TPS 171532